Why I Left
Canada

Leopold Infeld

Why I Left Canada

Reflections on Science and
Politics

Translated by Helen Infeld
Edited with Introduction and Notes by
Lewis Pyenson

McGill — Queen's University Press   Montreal and London
1978

This book has been published with the help of a grant from the
Social Sciences Research Council of Canada using funds provided by
the Canada Council. It was translated from material in *Szkice
przeszłości* (Warsaw, 1964) and *Kordian i ja* (Warsaw, 1968) published
by Państwowy Instytut Wydawniczy.

Design by Peter Maher
Printed in Canada

Contents

Illustrations

Illustrations

Acknowledgements

Among those who helped in various ways with this edition of Leopold Infeld's later writings are H. S. M. Coxeter, Eryk Infeld, James MacLachlan, Alfred T. Mitchell, Susan Sheets-Pyenson, Christie Vance, and Peter White. Maria Jastrzębowski verified the translation typed by Lucyna Piątek. Margery Simpson of McGill–Queen's University Press and Barbara Borkowska and Andrzej Mierzejewski of the Polish Authors' Agency provided prompt and sensitive editorial assistance. Otto Nathan and Helen Dukas authenticated extracts from the letters of Albert Einstein, and the Estate of Albert Einstein has generously consented to the publication of this material.

While this book was in press notification was received of the sudden death of Leopold Infeld's friend and colleague Alfred Schild. An expert in relativity physics, he followed this edition of the writings of his former teacher with interest. By a sad twist of fate, it was not given to him to see the finished product.

Foreword

When I first met Leopold Infeld in January 1942, he had been in
Toronto for three and a half years and had made it his home. Wherever he was he could come to terms with his surroundings and make
his presence felt whether in a room or a city. I became at the same
time Leopold's student and friend. He never treated me as a sub-
ordinate in spite of the differences in our position and age. We were
both interested in asking new questions and searching our minds for
new answers. In this we were equal. Of course he knew far more
than I, and his brilliant and penetrating intellect greatly influenced
my life during the next few years.

We met almost daily to work together, far more often than is
common in a professor-student relationship. At most of these meetings
he would outline his latest approach to our current problem. With
great enthusiasm he would explain that a new perspective had dis-
solved all our difficulties and that the solution was childishly simple.

Then we would examine his arguments and his premises and eventually reach the flaws. He always came up with another idea. We moved forward, found the flaw, and moved back, but never quite back to the beginning; and so our work advanced by thrust and check and thrust again. Sometimes this took place as we walked in the university grounds. Often we went to his house and then spent an hour or two in his study. Helen would bring coffee and, when his own daily quota of cigarettes was consumed, we would smoke the handmade cigarettes which my wife Winnie had rolled that morning.

Leopold's work in physics occupied a large part, but not all, of his life. He enjoyed his family and his friends. There was nothing of the hermit in his makeup. He had an appetite for life and a curiosity about everything. He liked to gossip, to eat and drink, to discuss the world in all its aspects.

He and Helen naturally formed the centre of a lively intellectual group. Both expressed and defended their opinions with vigour, but they also kept their minds open and liked to discuss and consider the ideas of others. Their influence spread far more widely than that of the average university couple. There was something magnetic, even exotic, about the big, talkative, brilliant man and his equally intelligent and attractive wife. Toronto in those days was a rather provincial city, its spirits dampened by a long and bitter war. It was not a lively place and Infeld says in *Quest*: "It must be good to die in Toronto. The transition between life and death would be continuous, painless and scarcely noticeable in this silent town." But Leopold made his own excitement; he refused to settle down into a dull daily routine.

People who will not accept the status quo and want to change the things they feel are wrong in the world must often suffer indignities from those who sit smugly in their comfortable corners and feel that any change threatens their position and their self-image. It was the Infelds' fate, during their last year in Toronto, to suffer at the hands of the smug and the fearful. *Why I Left Canada* understates, I think, the deep hurt Canada inflicted on this humane and decent family. Mean and vicious people made their last days there miserable. Remembering the kindness and friendship they had enjoyed for a decade, Leopold left the last shabby Canadian chapter unwritten. He writes of the official, public attacks but not of the private campaign of harassment, often by anonymous phone calls, of which, even today, Helen speaks with bitterness.

And so they left Canada to help Poland in its tremendous struggle to rebuild and to rise again from the ashes Germany had left.

In the fall of 1959 Andrzej Trautman, Bill Thompson, Winnie, and I were waiting at the London airport for the Infeld's flight from Warsaw. Leopold had suffered a serious heart attack a few years before, and they were coming to England for Leopold's periodic medical check up. Winnie and I had not seen them for almost ten years. It was a shock to see Leopold's ashen face, to watch his halting walk aided by a cane, to hear his slow and slightly slurred speech. But after a short time we realized with great relief that his spirit had not changed at all.

Later, during a visit to Warsaw, Leopold told us that soon after the onset of his illness he had decided that any day his heart might stop, but that until that day came he would live as fully as he could. He had to give his body some attention—a nap every afternoon, a saltless diet, the pills which prevented the accumulation of water in his cells; but apart from these necessary precautions he refused to treat himself as an invalid. He might just as easily die in Warsaw as die abroad, he said. In the last nine years of his life, the Infelds travelled to several places outside Western Europe, to India, Texas, Greece, and Israel. In all these countries Leopold enjoyed observing new customs and making new friends.

Leopold Infeld was a distinguished theoretical physicist. During a short visit to Leipzig in the early thirties, he and van der Waerden wrote an important paper on the generalization of the spinor calculus and of Dirac's equation for the electron to general relativity theory. In 1934, he was awarded a Rockefeller fellowship to work at Cambridge. There he collaborated with Max Born on what is now known as the Born-Infeld theory. It was an attempt to explain the existence of elementary charged particles in terms of well-behaved solutions of nonlinear equations for the electromagnetic field.

In 1936 he accepted a research appointment at the Institute for Advanced Study in Princeton. He worked with Albert Einstein and Banesh Hoffmann on the equations of motion in general relativity, a problem which was to be his principal research interest for the rest of his life. The work showed that Einstein's theory of gravitation has a unique feature, that the field laws alone determine the motion of particles and that no independent laws of motion are needed. This beautiful result is intimately connected with the nonlinearity of the gravitational field equations. It should play an important part in the future development of the whole of theoretical physics. The work also gave the first satisfactory description of the motion of several particles in gravitational interaction, for example, the relativistic motion of a double star. In 1960, Infeld and his former student Jerzy Plebański published a treatise on the subject, *Motion and Relativity.*

As important as his own scientific achievements was Leopold's success as a teacher. He attracted some of the brightest young men to work with him, and many of his research students and his students' students now hold university professorships, particularly in Canada and Poland. This ability to bring out the very best in his younger collaborators was due, I believe, to a strong feeling of his own worth combined with an equally strong respect for the worth of others and for the integrity of their individual views. I remember vividly and with gratitude two pieces of advice he gave me when I was completing my Ph.D. work: "Be generous to your students and be generous in giving them credit for their work; always try to gather around you those whom you think better than yourself." Leopold practised what he preached.

Leopold was convinced that it was the duty of scientists and other intellectuals to concern themselves with the state of the world, to make moral judgments, and to speak out openly on public issues. Again he practised what he preached, and often this took a great deal of courage. In Canada he spoke in favour of the post-war communist government in Poland at a time when such views were highly un-popular in the West. In Poland he led a movement of scholars and scientists for greater personal and intellectual freedom at a time when it was dangerous to express such views openly. He was one of the original signers of the Einstein-Russell manifesto of 1955 which led to the Pugwash Movement on Science and Public Affairs, an his-torically important step on the road to restraint and perhaps to nuclear disarmament.

Peter Bergmann concludes his obituary of Leopold Infeld in *Physics Today* by saying: "With his death all of us lose a distinguished colleague, and many a wise friend." I know that Winnie and I and our children feel this keenly, and we miss him.

ALFRED SCHILD
Austin, Texas

Introduction

By a series of strange circumstances, I did not become a leather merchant in Cracow and I did not die during the war in the ghetto of Cracow as did most of my family and almost all of my friends. This is due more to my luck and character than to my ability.

Leopold Infeld, "As I See it."

INFELD, THEORETICAL PHYSICS, AND POLITICS

Like others of his generation who became great scientific or intellectual figures, Leopold Infeld issued from central Europe at the time of material transformation and rising expectations that led into the twentieth century. It is not the intensity of Infeld's struggle to become a theoretical physicist, succeeding against all likelihood, that is striking in his own accounts; many others to whom events were less kind may

I

also claim to have contributed to human understanding. Neither is Infeld's talent as one of the most perceptive inside observers of twentieth-century theoretical physics unexpected, even if noteworthy in an age of mediocre autobiographical apologies by other scientists. Rather, most extraordinary in Infeld's final vision is his compelling faith in humanity.

Infeld was born in a Jewish ghetto in Krakow in 1898. His father was wealthy enough to keep a servant for the family's modest apartment. After having been educated in a Jewish commercial school, Infeld persuaded his parents to let him prepare for the university entrance examinations. These he passed on the eve of the First World War. After his father had bribed local officials to release him from active service in the Austrian army, Infeld could regularly attend lectures in physics at the Jagiellonian University in Krakow. He received his doctorate from Krakow in 1921 as the Polish Republic's first theoretical physicist.

Upon graduation Infeld had no prospects of employment. A few chairs in theoretical physics existed at Polish universities, but these political appointments were in practice closed to Jews. In his essay on Władysław Natanson, which is translated in this book, Infeld remarks on the restrictive system of academic succession:

> To attract students, to train them—this was looked upon in old Krakow as vulgar, smacking of the kindergarten. It was considered proper to select one student during a lifetime, make him a docent, and let him wait quietly for his professor to retire or die. In order that he might wait not too impatiently, he should be a person of some means, politically reliable—which meant a Krakow conservative—and be of good family. If such a person has already been found, then Pauli's exclusion principle applies: the place is filled and no one else can aspire to it.[1]

Infeld spent the next years as a schoolmaster in the provinces and then in Warsaw. He managed to be appointed assistant and finally docent at the University of Lwów. In 1933, following the death of his wife Halina, he obtained a Rockefeller fellowship to study at Cambridge with Max Born and at Leipzig with Bartel L. van der Waerden. Returning to Poland and finding no possibility of succeeding to a chair, he left in 1936 to work with Einstein at the Institute for Advanced Study in

Princeton. This voyage marked the beginning of a thirteen-year absence from Poland.

In 1938, at the age of forty, Infeld was offered the opportunity to begin a new career at the University of Toronto. His autobiography *Quest* reveals that he received this call with mixed emotions.[2] He was beginning his career once more at a time in life when many other theoretical physicists hold chairs and have their best work behind them. Infeld was promoted rapidly and trained many students. Despite the presence of brilliant mathematical colleagues, however, his own speciality withered. His Department of Applied Mathematics merged with the Department of Mathematics. The University of Toronto expressed little interest in Infeld's desire to create a strong centre of theoretical physics.

Canadian indifference to theoretical physics reflected broader trends. Though theoretical physicists were active elsewhere, this discipline was not favoured by many of its host institutions. Before the Second World War physics remained the only scientific discipline to have produced a speciality devoted exclusively to theory. Theoretical physicists sought to provide a framework for unifying the laws and phenomena discovered by many widely separated research programs.[3] Since the time of its creation, theoretical physics represented only a small part of the educational effort in science. In Germany, where the discipline first established roots, fewer than 7 percent of all doctorates granted in the years around 1900 went to physics; only a small fraction of these were in theoretical physics.[4] Though of increasing relevance for other disciplines, theoretical physics remained relatively neglected in a period that saw the rise of large-budget research teams in experimental physics.

As a rare theoretical physicist training doctoral students in Canada, Infeld was discouraged. Nevertheless, disciplinary isolation was not behind his decision in 1950 to leave Canada for Poland. Infeld was sympathetic to the new Workers' State in Poland; he extensively denounced American nuclear blackmail; he collaborated closely with Einstein. Stimulated by McCarthyism in Washington and by the Gouzenko affair in Ottawa, conservative critics denounced Infeld as a potential traitor to the Canadian people. The leader of the opposition asked, if Infeld were permitted to go to Warsaw University in 1950 to lecture during a leave of absence, as he planned, would he not

3

provide the communists with atomic secrets? As with many others in North America, Infeld received too little help too late. RCMP surveillance and other harassment made it impossible for him to continue his research. He decided to accept the Warsaw invitation, realizing that he might never be allowed to return to Canada. When he arrived in Poland, the Canadian ambassador asked him to surrender his Canadian passport. Later, his two children were stripped of their Canadian citizenship by an order in council, the only time such a procedure has ever been applied to native-born Canadians.

INFELD AND EINSTEIN

Infeld is Boswell for the mature Einstein, the wise old lion who seized the imagination of our age. In 1936, Infeld saw Einstein in Princeton again, after many years of separation. In two paragraphs he presents perhaps the fullest, most beautiful portrait of Einstein in his late fifties:

> I knocked at the door of 209 and heard a loud "herein." When I opened the door I saw a hand stretched out energetically. It was Einstein, looking older than when I had met him in Berlin, older than the elapsed sixteen years should have made him. His long hair was grey, his face tired and yellow, but he had the same radiant deep eyes. He wore the brown leather jacket in which he has appeared in so many pictures. (Someone had given it to him to wear when sailing, and he liked it so well that he dressed in it every day.) His shirt was without a collar, his brown trousers creased, and he wore shoes without socks. I expected a brief private conversation, questions about my crossing, Europe, Born, etc. Nothing of the kind:
> "Do you speak German?"
> "Yes," I answered.
> "Perhaps I can tell you on what I am working."
> Quietly he took a piece of chalk, went to the blackboard, and started to deliver a perfect lecture. The calmness with which Einstein spoke was striking. There was nothing of the restlessness of a scientist who, explaining the problems with which he has lived for years, assumes that they are equally familiar to the listener and proceeds quickly with his exposition. Before going into details Einstein sketched the philosophical background for the problems on which he was working. Walking slowly and with dignity around the room, going to the

blackboard from time to time to write down mathematical equations, keeping a dead pipe in his mouth, he formed his sentences perfectly. Everything that he said could have been printed as he said it and every sentence would make perfect sense. The exposition was simple, profound and clear.[5]

Infeld is most successful in describing the values Einstein brought to his work. Infeld's Einstein, though he came to lose confidence "in the merit of ever impressive confirmations of theories, whenever questions of principle are involved," still claimed "strict adherence to logical simplicity."[6] Einstein's tools came from mathematics. As a young man, he thought that mathematics was at best incidental to the development of new syntheses of nature's laws. Later, after having formulated the covariant field equations of general relativity, he came to believe that mathematics might provide a heuristic basis for new physical theories. Nevertheless, through Einstein's entire scientific career runs the thread that mathematics was insufficient to dictate the nature of physical reality. "God does not care about our mathematical difficulties," Infeld cites Einstein in *Quest*, "He integrates empirically."[7] Mathematics for Einstein constituted a language which had always to be used and then transcended before truth could be fathomed. He wrote to Infeld in 1946, "Please don't be angry with me that I have written you so infrequently; the devilish passion to find a solution for these most difficult problems has held me pitilessly in its clutches and has forced me to make desperate efforts to overcome the mathematical difficulties."[8] The tendency was great, Einstein felt, to use mathematical formalism as a substitute for knowledge. Physical intuition, the sixth sense Einstein mentioned in his *Autobiographical Notes*, remained the key to understanding.[9]

Central to Infeld's narrative is the intensity and clarity of Einstein's intellectual power. "There is a most vital mechanism which constantly turns his brain. It is the sublimated vital force. Sometimes it is even painful to watch."[10] This characterization derived from several years of close collaboration on the nature of motion in the general theory of relativity. The result of Infeld's and Einstein's work, well known among specialists in field theory but not widely popularized, was truly a joint effort, as Einstein himself insisted later.[11] It is also perhaps the episode in Einstein's creative endeavour that is best documented.

Einstein had suggested a common project that involved deriving the equations of motion from the gravitational field equations, and, in addition, uniting the gravitational and the quantum theories. This proposed course was to be a major innovation, for in the general theory of relativity the motion of mass points was governed by geodesics in space-time, and the metrics were derived separately from the field equations. In the period between 1936 and 1938 Einstein and Infeld worked on these problems together, frequently at each other's side for entire afternoons. Infeld was skeptical at first about both of Einstein's contentions, and he luxuriated in his own contrariness. A critical attitude and an independent spirit were essential if his collaboration with Einstein were to succeed. Infeld recalls in *Quest*:

> I know that there is nothing so dangerous in science as blind acceptance of authorities and dogmas. My own mind must remain for me the highest authority. Nearly every understanding is gained by a painful struggle in which belief and disbelief are dramatically interwoven. I wanted to make this point quite clear to Einstein.[12]

When Infeld first came to believe intuitively that the equations of motion were indeed contained in the field equations, his whole attitude changed, and he began to work with great enthusiasm. But he still doubted that the field equations could be related to the quantum theory. Skepticism formed the basis of his contribution to the joint effort, for, at last, he was able to convince Einstein that the gravitational equations could not yield quantum restrictions for motion.[13]

The collaboration was enormously difficult for Infeld. He felt constantly submerged in a flood of new ideas. "Sometimes after we separated I would think in the night about our last discussion, and a new idea would strike me, illuminating the subject from a new angle. Next day I would rush to Einstein, often only to find that he had come to the same conclusion and was still further along."[14] Once the general theory was established, specific calculations had to be undertaken. This was Infeld's task. Although Einstein was interested in the difficulties that appeared, he took little part in the actual work. Einstein believed that the essential part of the problem had been solved. "Once a work is finished," Infeld remarks elsewhere in *Quest*, Einstein's "interest in it ceases."[15]

The collaboration of Einstein with Infeld came to provide the focus for both their lives. At the time they were working, Einstein's wife Elsa was in the terminal stage of her last illness. The first floor of the Einstein residence had been arranged for her deathbed. On the second floor, in the study, Einstein and Infeld would work for many hours together. Einstein cared deeply for his wife, but death was something he knew he could not change. The pursuit of his work was his reason for being, and only in this way, by directing himself to what he believed to be fundamental, did he feel that he could cheat death. In *Quest*, Infeld describes how, after Elsa died, Einstein, more pale and more tired than before, continued to work mornings in his office. Recalling the death of his own wife Halina, Infeld marvelled at Einstein's composure.

Nearly a decade afterwards, in the late forties, Einstein and Infeld worked together once more. Einstein was almost seventy. During the war, Infeld had worked on problems unrelated to general relativity and had spent much time popularizing science. The two theoretical physicists had not seen each other for nine years. At Einstein's suggestion, they began to work again on the problem of motion in general relativity. Einstein wanted to demonstrate that the approximation technique they had developed could be extended indefinitely. The initial stages of collaboration were carried out by an intense correspondence. Then, Infeld relates, he thought of introducing a virtual gravitational dipole to facilitate the calculation. When he convinced his former student Alfred Schild that the approach was feasible, Infeld wrote to Einstein, who responded by explaining his own ideas without mentioning the dipoles. Infeld answered by criticizing Einstein's work and asked him to reread his letter explaining the dipole method. This time Einstein answered favourably:

> You are quite right with your objections to my remarks about the divergence of the approximating equations. I write you only today because I had still hoped to find the letter in which you had offered some proof for your theories. But I was not successful. I had not read your letter with sufficient care because I had no doubts about the justification of my own thoughts which were based on breaking down the Bianchi identity. And so I should like to ask you to send me a copy of your remarks.[16]

7

Einstein, sure that his way was more fruitful, had lost Infeld's letter. Infeld decided that a visit to Princeton would clarify the matter. The meeting actually took place in a New York clinic where Einstein was under observation and treatment. Einstein sensed that he would not live much longer. Infeld deferred to his collaborator:

> I knew Einstein well and I knew that it didn't do to interrupt him. He talked about the trouble he still had with his work. Apparently he had completely forgotten my letter. When he finished I asked him to let me explain how I believed I had overcome the difficulty. I got out only two sentences—about the fact that it is necessary to add the gravitational dipoles, that they guarantee the integrability of the equations and that the later removal of the dipoles gives the equations of motion. As always when he was thinking, he began to stroke his moustache and then ask questions. I knew that this was his method, that he did not like lectures, only discussion. When I had answered three questions Einstein exclaimed enthusiastically, "Well, then, our problems are solved. Why didn't you write me about it?"[17]

Einstein pursued his work with singleminded purpose.

The quality that Einstein dearly sought in collaboration, as in friendship, was obstinate criticism. It was precisely this quality that Einstein valued in his early collaboration with Jakob Johann Laub and Erwin Finlay Freundlich, in his friendship with Paul Ehrenfest, and in his work with Infeld.[18] Einstein loved Infeld for his ebullient, critical approach to theoretical physics. The spirit Infeld brought to his work was uncharacteristic of that radiated by many other professors. Infeld's world was far from the academic bourgeoisie.

As Infeld was aware, considerable moral and emotional strength was required to work as an intellectual in Wilhelmian or Weimar Germany and not appropriate at the same time the usual worldviews endemic to German academic society. Deciding to become a non-establishment intellectual carried the possibility of being frozen on the periphery of academic life in German-speaking and Eastern Europe. Infeld points out that even unusual powers of self-reliance were often not enough to prevent a disastrous erosion of self-confidence. Einstein working at the Patent Office in Berne, Laub as an unemployed physicist in Würzburg, Ehrenfest without a position in Russia, Infeld as a schoolmaster in Konin, all were theoretical physicists on the periphery of the physics profession. Although they were for a time outsiders in a highly structured discipline, it would be a mistake to claim that Einstein and his close friends belonged to an alternative culture.[19] They were not science-oriented bohemians, nor were they social revolutionaries like the astronomer Anton Pannekoek, the mathematician Gerrit Mannoury, or the philologist Rudolf Grossmann.[20] Unconventional philosophical socialists, whose belief in social justice and critical thought were both paramount, comes closer to the mark.

At the time he collaborated with Infeld, Einstein sensed that most professional physicists regarded him as a ridiculous figure. Only a handful of people would bother to read Einstein's latest papers, Infeld remarks. Why, then, should Einstein's enterprise have seized with such force the imagination of an age? Infeld suggests that Einstein's renown appeared as a manifestation of social psychology after the First World War. The verification of general relativity by the Royal Astronomical Society expeditions of 1919 reflected "abstract thought carrying the human mind far away from the sad and disappointing reality." Predicted by a German scientist and confirmed by English astronomers, general relativity seemed to indicate a new era of cooperation.[21] Infeld believes that Einstein's fame persisted because of a popular image that remained true in its essentials:

> Everything that Einstein did, everything for which he stood, was always consistent with the primary picture of him in the mind of the people. . . . He was like a saint with two halos around his head. One was formed of ideas of justice and progress, the other of abstract ideas about physical theories which, the more abstruse they were, the more impressive they seemed to the ordinary man.[22]

In his *Autobiographical Notes* Einstein remarks that he was, to use Infeld's imagery, a secular monk contemplating the extrapersonal world.[23] Evidence for any duality in his spirit is lacking. Infeld remarks later that Einstein had always believed that scientific work was "a matter of character."[24] Einstein's science was a profoundly moral undertaking. Beauty, truth, goodness, justice—these are the interchangeable attributes of Spinoza's god, and perhaps in their relatedness lay the unity of Einstein's genius.

Introduction

INFELD'S QUEST

In 1937 Infeld's fellowship at the Institute for Advanced Study had expired and he faced returning to a darkening Poland. Although Einstein intervened on his behalf, Infeld could not obtain an extension of his appointment. To earn enough money to stay at Princeton for another year, Infeld suggested to Einstein that they write a popular history of physical thought for English-language readers. As the work progressed, it became increasingly less popularly oriented. The first part of the manuscript outlined the "new and revolutionary ideas" introduced into physics during the last half of the nineteenth century by Michael Faraday, James Clerk Maxwell, and Heinrich Hertz. In the second part, Einstein and Infeld described "the break brought about in science" in the twentieth-century that "gradually gained clarity and strength."[25] Emphasis was placed on the logic of physical developments, Einstein and Infeld recognizing at the same time that contemporary physics was characterized by major conceptual discontinuities. Completed without a title the manuscript became *The Evolution of Physics: The Growth of Ideas From Early Concepts to Relativity and Quanta*, through a compromise between the authors and the American publisher.[26] At the time Einstein remarked to his friend Maurice Solovine that a more appropriate title for the book was the one used in the 1938 German translation that was published in Leiden,[27] *Physics as an Adventure in Understanding*.[28] Einstein believed the German title emphasized the psychological, subjective aspect of his and Infeld's story. The word evolution is out of place in the English title because the book explains *revolutionary* developments in nineteenth- and twentieth-century physics. Einstein and Infeld's English reader was led to expect a respectable story describing the regular progress of physical ideas.

Three years later, Infeld used the word evolution in the subtitle of his principal literary achievement, his autobiography. Despite the breaks and reversals of his career, he wanted to emphasize the continuity of his own individual experience. *Quest: The Evolution of a Scientist* chronicles his unusual apprenticeship. Justification of his scientific accomplishments was of minor importance in Infeld's conception of the work. He sought above all to relay his doubts, confusions, and daily impressions about the science and politics that he had experienced in Europe and America. *Quest* ends with the discovery of Leopold Infeld on the verge of a new beginning in Toronto. The autobiography tells only part of his life. Some of his later experiences are relayed in the present book.

Quest is a remarkable achievement, a literary statement made the more compelling because it is written in Infeld's fourth language. It marks the beginning of a new role for the scientist as a writer. Before *Quest*, scientific autobiography as a genre was often little more than scientific apology. After obligatory references to youth and family, the author described his life as a confluence of scientific ideas, scientific influences, and scientific accomplishments. Nineteenth-century English autobiographies, for example, those of Charles Darwin, Thomas Henry Huxley, Alfred Russel Wallace, Herbert Spencer, and Charles Babbage, provide vivid insight into how Victorian scientists projected respectable images. Their creative psychology is retrievable only indirectly. In a similar way, many of the autobiographies that appeared in early twentieth-century Germany, those of Wilhelm Ostwald, Wilhelm Wien, and August Föppl, are really memoirs. The reader is presented with an image of the German academic as a cultural leader and member of the bourgeoisie. In both the English and the German cases, interaction between author and reader is one-dimensional. The literary medium is used to transfer a well-prepared picture rather than to moderate between author and reader.

Although Infeld was not the first to emphasize psychological development in autobiography, *Quest* is one of the first successful treatments of this kind by a scientist. Infeld's achievement is revealed by contrasting *Quest* against two other autobiographical attempts. The first is to be found in the posthumous memoirs of the mathematician Sonya Kovalevsky; the second, and an alternative pole of reference, is the autobiography of Henry Adams.

Kovalevsky's account is predictable and conventional.[29] It offers no indication that the Russian noble's daughter, whose emotional lines are so carefully revealed, will become the greatest woman mathematician of the nineteenth century. Kovalevsky chooses not to speak of intellectual affairs. The reader is left without a clear idea of the narrator's vision of herself, in contrast to Infeld's doubt-ridden narrative. *The Education of Henry Adams* illustrates the pole opposite to that presented by Kovalevsky: transcendental reflections on society as it impinges upon and subtly, continuously transforms the author's ego. Henry Adams offers possibly the most important statement about science and society to be delivered on the eve of the special theory of relativity and quantum physics.[30] Central to Adams' text is the enormous emotional gap separating the "virgin" of humanism and faith from the "dynamo" of science and technology. Adams is one of the last premodern men, anticipating the intellectual, social, and political upheavals of the twentieth century with wonder and hesitation, but without fear. It is just this other-worldly teleology—Adams' detachment from the events that gently cajole his mind's eye according to some unspecified, internal, absolute mechanism—that the reader identifies as incomplete.

Transcending the difficulties posed by both Kovalevsky and Adams, Infeld's *Quest* lies near the beginning of a new literature. The autobiographical writings of such figures as James Watson and Werner Heisenberg follow, more or less directly, in Infeld's path. In presenting his story, Infeld brings the theoretical physicist down from the clouds. He is seen as an ordinary man, with ordinary wants and vanities, who seeks to fathom the laws of the physical universe. He is driven to his career in the same way that the artist or the writer is driven to his task. To work in theoretical physics Infeld sustains injustice and poverty. He pursues his science at the same time that his world—the world that made the discipline of theoretical physics possible—slides into barbarism.

Infeld's self-quest is continued in several of the essays constituting the present book. It may be better understood in contrast to the autobiographies of Sigmund Freud and Albert Einstein, whose work influenced Infeld's career. The reader is struck by the extraordinary singleminded purpose in the stories of Einstein and Freud. For either one to have recounted events irrelevant to his life's work would have been to disappoint the reader and ill serve his own cause. The process of stripping the author's persona to reveal his deeper self is at once continuous and complete. For Freud, creator of modern psychoanalysis, anything other than his moving intellectual history would be anticlimax.[31] Einstein insisted on a similar position. A third of the way through his *Autobiographical Notes*, Einstein suddenly says: "the essential in the being of a man of my type lies precisely in *what* he thinks and *how* he thinks, not in what he does or suffers."[32] Nothing would have been farther from Einstein's spirit than for him to have detailed the everyday occurrences of his youth, his emotional needs and strivings.

Freud and Einstein present convincing self-told stories because of who they are, and, indeed, because they detail the genesis of self-consciousness while omitting triviality. In their cases, unlike in Infeld's, the distinction between intellectual and psychological components is not of central importance for the reader. Their narratives are complete and consistent without telling about their reaction to everyday affairs, and for this reason the reader finds them remote and awe-inspiring. On the contrary, Infeld tells what it is like to be a theoretical scientist. The reader breathes with him as he walks through Princeton, Toronto, and Warsaw. Even Infeld's occasional vanities and failings only serve to bring about a more sympathetic rendering of the theoretical scientist at mid-century.

Presented in this volume are the later reflections of Leopold Infeld. The chapter "Oppenheimer" is taken from *Kordian i ja* (Warsaw, 1968). The rest comes from *Szkice z przeszłości* (Warsaw, 1964). The chapter "Einstein" has been shortened somewhat in translation, as parts of the original text were adapted from Infeld's autobiography *Quest* (Garden City, N.Y., 1941). One long sequence from "Einstein," where Infeld describes the Polish and Soviet reaction during the early 1950s to his work with Einstein, has been included in the chapter "Poland." With these exceptions the translations correspond precisely to the original material.

Canada
and
Poland

PLATE I. Leopold Infeld in Princeton.

Canada

I well remember the shabby, small, two-story building at 47 St. George Street in Toronto. It has since been torn down. But then, twenty years ago, it still stood, uncared-for, unrepaired for many years. It housed the Department of Applied Mathematics—that is to say of Theoretical Physics—of the University of Toronto, where I spent the years 1938 to 1950. On the ground floor was a small lecture room. One flight up was the office of the head of department which was also used for conferences. Above this, under the roof, was my room. In addition, the building contained three offices of the other professors and small cubbyholes for the assistants. This department had originally been set up especially for its head, J[ohn] L[ighton] Synge, who had been at Trinity College, Dublin. He was more talented as a mathematician than as a physicist. Approximately my age, he was widely known and highly esteemed for his great industry and mathematical ability. It was known to happen that after an evening's discussion he would come in the next day with a work all written up, neatly and without mistakes. A Fellow of the Royal Society of London, he was an excellent lecturer (and no doubt still is) and had an extremely upright, if somewhat dry, character.

In Canada we felt the war very little. Restaurants functioned almost normally; prices rose only a little; there was plenty of everything and the one evidence of the war was the appearance of enlisted men in uniform. British evacuees brought with them tales of falling bombs and sleepless nights and the very few refugees from Poland, who came through the Soviet Union and Japan, told about the suffering of my native land and its people.

Professor Synge and I discussed how we might help the war effort. He went to Ottawa to see General McNaughton, who had been the head of the Canadian armed forces during the First World War and then was the head of a scientific institution in Ottawa called the National Research Council. General McNaughton handed him some old notes taken during the First World War, giving many different kinds of figures on artillery fire, and asked that we put them in order and make a mathematical analysis of the material. Together with several other colleagues, we set to work. We met every Saturday and tried to find a formula to fit the given values. Several months later we completed the job and wrote a report in which we analysed the out-dated information. Professor Synge sent it to General McNaughton. We were all sure that the report would be thrown straight into the wastepaper basket.

It happened that two or three years later I met a former student of mine who was then a lieutenant in the Canadian Army, and he told me that our work had been printed in a semi-secret publication. And that was not the end of the story.

Sometime later, I attended a dinner where General [Andrew George] McNaughton gave a speech, after which a mutual acquaintance introduced us. Searching for a topic of conversation, I said that I was one of the authors of the work done with Professor Synge. The general was very pleased to hear this and told me that he had learned from a Soviet general that this work was the basic ballistic study in the Soviet Army. Moreover, McNaughton told me that by our work we had saved many lives. When I reported this to

Professor Synge, he, like me, hesitated to believe that our analysis of outdated figures could have saved a single life.

When the "phony" war came to an end, the National Research Council asked us to undertake war work. We had a meeting in Ottawa —several scientists including Synge and myself, and high army dignitaries. After dinner we were scheduled to visit an army research centre. That day, Professor Synge told me that it might be better if I returned to Toronto and not waste time looking at laboratories. I found this odd suggestion hard to understand. Finally, Synge said hesitantly, "I can't lie to you—I must tell you the truth." It turned out that I had not been "cleared" by the Royal Canadian Mounted Police. I was sure that the reason for this was my left-wing views but Synge informed me that the Colonel who talked with him said it was because I had relatives in Poland. True, I was a Canadian citizen, but, should the Nazis wish to obtain secrets from me, they could do so by torturing my family.

Yet a few months later I was cleared and took part in the theoretical work on radar wave guides, this being the one field in which I ever had information that was at any time secret. We worked together, holding meetings in Ottawa and Toronto; we wrote papers only issued confidentially.

After the war these papers were declassified—that is, they were released for publication and did appear in scientific journals. They were not so very important but still they were not without some value.[1]

At the same time that we did research on radar there was a group in Montreal working on nuclear physics and the construction of the atomic bomb.[2] I was barely aware of this at the time and had no idea how far they had progressed. I had nothing to do with this activity and knew only that one of my students took part in it.

When I was still of school age in Krakow I was deeply impressed by the touching story of the young French mathematician Evariste Galois told me by my old and kindly professor, F. Brablec. I found it extremely dramatic and tragic. The twenty-year-old boy was killed in a duel; on the last night of his life he hastily wrote for posterity the scientific notes from which emerged today's modern algebra. I always wanted to know more about his story. Later, when I was in America working with Einstein, I came upon E. T. Bell's *Men of Mathematics*.[3] It contained sketches of the lives of a number of the greatest mathematicians, including Galois. My interest grew. I decided that some time I would return to this story and learn more about it from original sources. Quite accidentally this came to pass.

One day the editor of my book *Quest* visited me and proposed that I write a new book, preferably biographical; he suggested in the name of the publishers that it be a life of Copernicus. To tell the truth, Copernicus did not interest me very much. It seemed to me a trivial thing to write so that the English-speaking world would know that Copernicus was a Pole. And I saw little of tragedy in his life. Besides, in America it would be difficult to find original sources. But I recalled my interest in Galois and suggested to the editor that I might try to write the story of his life.

I began to look for sources in Toronto. The university library helped me and so did many American libraries. I found a number of materials previously unknown and uncited, but still many aspects of his life remained unclear. Professor Synge, who knew about my work, told me he had heard that the American millionaire William Marshall Bullitt of Louisville, Kentucky, had collected everything having to do with Galois's life. His agents, through his relative the American Ambassador in Paris, had searched for these documents and he had amassed a unique collection.

I wrote to Mr. Bullitt who, in return, very kindly invited me to visit him for a few days and to examine his collection. This was near the end of the war when I had little war work to do. I accepted his invitation and had my first fairly intimate association with a real American millionaire. I know that it will not be quite nice of me to tell in detail about those few days and how I spent them. It will not be polite of me, for Mr. Bullitt was very hospitable, receiving me very pleasantly. I stayed with him the whole time in his impressive home— occupying two rooms with a bath, surrounded by beautiful portraits of men and women of olden times. I don't know whether these were real or imaginary people.

When I reached Louisville, it was already very warm. The trip was tiring and I arrived worn-out and dirty. When I telephoned to Mr. Bullitt, he asked me to come to the skyscraper which housed his insurance company. There Mr. Bullitt invited me to have a bath in a luxurious bathroom adjoining his office.

"Today," he said, "we won't work. We'll just eat supper together and then go to the Derby. I have a box there and I've said we're coming."

We left the office in his high-powered car. He drove and shouted aggressively at anyone who got in his way. The car had license number 1. On the way we talked but little since he was old, having passed his eightieth year, and he was a little deaf. Conversation was difficult. He uttered the brilliant words:

"If Galois were alive today and saw this car, what would he say?"

I was tired and to this foolish question gave an equally foolish answer:

"Some things haven't changed."

"What? What?" asked Mr. Bullitt.

"Some things haven't changed," I shouted again.

"For instance . . .?"

I didn't know how to end this silly conversation.

"The fight for freedom," I answered.

"What? What?"

"The fight for freedom," I repeated, fully aware that the talk was becoming quite idiotic.

"Oh, yes. You're right. Today, too, we have a fight for freedom against Roosevelt." This was during the Roosevelt-Dewey campaign.

We reached his home for supper. I remember that he had corn on the cob for the first course. I have since asked many people in America how millionaires eat corn. No one has been able to give me the correct answer. They only knew that millionaires have the cob cut into pieces and that they have two silver prongs to hold them with. But no one seems to know about the special gadget used to loosen the kernels so that they then fall into the mouth like ripe apples from a tree. Each of us had such a gadget made of silver. With the later courses we were offered two small trays with forty condiments, mostly from India, of which I was familiar only with salt and pepper.

After supper we went to the Derby. When we parked the car, Mr. Bullitt had a long talk with the attendant, asking him to place it so that Mr. Bullitt could get it out easily at any moment and so that no other cars would be near it. He said: "If you're good to me, I'll be good to you." I was sure that these words, repeated several times, meant that the attendant would be highly rewarded. At the least his son would be sent to college and he himself would receive a hundred dollars. Later it turned out that instead of the usual 25-cent fee, the attendant received 50 cents!

In Mr. Bullitt's loge were a number of people. Some were beautiful women—I think his grandchildren. Horses walked about pulling carts, and the people from time to time stood up and applauded, apparently without reason. I had not the least idea what the Derby was all about.

I listened to the women's talk. They were discussing the make of their airplanes, just as the women of the middle class talk about their cars.

After the Derby we returned to the Bullitt house. We looked over his library with its thousands and thousands of volumes. It was a huge library, and truly beautiful. I wanted to find a book to read in bed but there were so many that it was difficult to make a choice. Finally I selected several and went upstairs to sleep. My rooms were furnished with antiques and had portraits on the walls. I still remember that in the bathroom the toilet paper was rose-coloured and perfumed. The window frames creaked so much in the wind that I was unable to sleep in the midst of all the abundance and luxury.

Next day at about eleven in the morning we went to the office. Three of Mr. Bullitt's secretaries stood at attention—one poured water for him, another dropped aspirin into the water, and a third stood ready with a pad and pen. He graciously drank the water with aspirin and dictated a letter, after which all three ladies left. Mr. Bullitt then showed me his library on Galois; I looked over his collection and at the same time heard his telephone conversation. I don't know to whom he was talking but he was saying that somebody else pleased him very much and should have a better position. Then he telephoned to still another person to say that somebody did not please him and should be released from his job. On his huge desk was a whole collection of pencils on each of which was printed, "Vote for Dewey."

After two days, my work finished, and tired by the millionaire atmosphere, I wanted to go to New York and then to Toronto. Mr. Bullitt asked me how I wished to travel. I answered that I would go by train. He was amazed—why not by plane? At that time it was impossible to get a seat on a plane without reserving it weeks in advance, and even then it might be withdrawn. It was extremely likely that some colonel or other, with priority, would be assigned the seat. I explained this. He replied that he would get a place for me. He phoned someone and a reservation was made immediately. I left by plane. It was actually my first airplane trip. Mr. Bullitt himself took me to the airport and we were ten minutes late—driving madly on the way—in order to show me that the plane would wait especially for him. Even at my departure, I had to witness how important he was.

The trip was wonderful. The plane flew smoothly and the sight of Washington and the Capitol lit up was thrilling.

When I landed in New York after two and a half hours instead of the twenty-four by train, I felt worn out from my stay in Louisville and my first encounter with an American millionaire.

With my book about Galois I had much trouble, mostly because of my own stupidity! Finally it appeared in America and made but little stir.[4] Of all the capitalist countries, it had a greater influence, strangely, only in Japan, where it went through two printings. But it was more popular in the socialist countries, especially in Poland and the Soviet Union.

Einstein liked the book. After reading it he sent me the following letter:

I am very much excited over your book on Galois. It is a psychological masterpiece, a convincing historical picture, an expression of love for human greatness which was combined with an exceptionally honest character.

You may submit these remarks, translated into good English, to your publisher for whatever use he may make of them. These are not some casual remarks of mine; I honestly admire your work. I am particularly impressed with the convincing description of the dark background of the story, convincing because of the timelessness of the circumstances of that unusual man. This is what probably made you write the book. I fully understand it.[5]

While the war was still on, Professor Synge left Canada to take a better position in the United States. He later ended up at the Institute for Advanced Studies in his native Dublin. Our own small department, which had been independent, became part of the Department of Mathematics with Professor [Samuel] Beatty as its head. Since Dean Beatty is important in this story, it would be well to say a few words about him. He was an older man, more an administrator than a mathematician, in general very decent but capable of doing something unfair more through stupidity than bad character. Dean Beatty had little understanding for the scientific work done by those under him. Still, relations between us were good, even very good and sometimes cordial —largely because of his liberal attitude.

I believe that I have considerably more pedagogical than research ability. I was very anxious to use it to build a strong centre of theoretical physics in Toronto. At the time it was the only place in Canada granting a doctorate in that field. During my whole time in Canada it remained the one place that trained theoretical physicists. But no one in Canada cared about it. The Ph.D.s I trained found positions in other Canadian centres or in the United States—never at the University of Toronto. To my urgent request that our group be enlarged, I received the answer from this very rich university: "No, we can't. We haven't the money." Finally, after long urging, the university agreed to hire the best Ph.D. I had produced in place of someone who had left for the U.S. After he had been with us for a year, a university in the States offered him a salary of $800 a year more. The young physicist then told me that he would gladly remain in Toronto if the university would raise his salary only $200 a year, as evidence that they really wanted him to stay. In spite of every effort to achieve this small increase, the President, Sidney Smith, refused.

Every province in Canada had its own university. The best-known were McGill University in Montreal and the University of Toronto. But the province of Manitoba also had its university at Winnipeg, the capital of the province. During the last days of the academic year, each university invited someone to deliver an address to the students who were graduating. I was sufficiently well known in Canada for the University in Winnipeg to invite me to be the speaker. For my theme I chose the danger inherent in the lack of respect for learning. I said that if the most brilliant people continued to leave Canada for the United States, then, eventually, according to biological laws, the intellectual level in Canada would go down and I added, in jest, "if for thousands of years this trend does not change, then Canada will become a nation of morons." That very day the local paper carried the headline: "Infeld Predicts Canada to Be Country of Morons."[6]

This lack of respect for scientific work, for the position of a professor, was characteristic of Canada and perhaps still more of the United States. It became more and more disturbing to me and I realized that I would not be able to change it. Actually, this situation changed only after the Soviet Union launched its first sputnik.

In New York, during the war, I met Julian Tuwim. His name is known to every child in Poland, but almost unknown outside the country because poetry is very difficult to translate. Many people in Poland, and I among them, regard him as the best Polish poet of our century, and second only to Adam Mickiewicz in all our Romantic literature that so abounded in fine poetry.

Tuwim barely escaped from the Nazis, coming to New York through Rumania, Italy, and France. A degree of friendship developed between us. In any case, speaking for myself, I felt close understanding mixed with admiration, even a sort of worship. In 1945 Tuwim spent his vacation in Toronto. Once when I visited him there, he asked me with great excitement, "Have you heard the latest? Truman has just announced that an atomic bomb has been dropped on a Japanese city, Hiroshima."

I was speechless. I had no idea that the United States would produce the atomic bomb so quickly and I certainly did not expect that they would drop it on Japan, which was so near defeat.

During the next few months the papers were full of often-repeated slogans and phrases: "The greatest discovery since the discovery of fire! May God permit us to keep the secret! We must guard this secret which only we know! While we keep the secret, we are secure. We must guard against spies who are trying to steal the secret!"

General Roberts, chief of the Manhattan Project, stated that the Russians would discover the secret for themselves only after twenty-five years, and perhaps never.[7] No one spoke out seriously in public against this dangerous and silly talk, except for me. It all began with an invitation from a group of professors, including the president of the university, to talk to them about the atomic bomb. I covered the related physics very quickly and then analysed all the idiotic slogans surrounding the bomb. I tried to explain that there was no secret of the atomic bomb, just as there is no secret to being a good husband, just as there are no secret laws of physics. The real secret, I explained, was that the thing was possible, and that circumstance ceased to be a secret with the explosion on Hiroshima. I went on to say that the Soviet Union also had good physicists and, without spying, could construct an atomic bomb after three or at most four years. With this speech I went to many places. I could not accept all the invitations I received to talk about the atomic bomb. I gave my lecture across the length and breadth of Canada, about fifty times. I also wrote a pamphlet about it.[8] Often I talked over the radio. I picked up quite a number of amusing incidents as a result. Probably the best is as follows. Once I gave a talk to very wealthy people in Toronto. Following my speech explaining that there was no secret of the atomic bomb, one bright member of the audience asked: "What should we do to keep the secret of the atomic bomb from Russia?"

A growing opposition to me was developing among those who hated what I had to say. If the Soviet Union could really make an atomic bomb in the time I predicted, then how did I know it? Didn't that mean that I had some kind of dangerous contact with them?

This opposition to me swelled in the next five years. Then, when I wanted to accept an invitation to my native land of Poland in 1950, it burst out in open attack. I was accused of wanting to give the secret of the atomic bomb, of which I had no idea, to a country "behind the iron curtain." As a result, the Royal Canadian Mounted Police dogged my footsteps and those of my family, we were annoyed by vicious telephone calls, and finally the University of Toronto suddenly cancelled my leave of absence to visit Europe. The net effect of all this was that I remained in Poland, where I still am after fifteen years. Thus, in a smaller way, my own life was changed by the explosion over Hiroshima.

Today, twenty years after the event, human beings are dying because of the two bombs dropped in 1945, and still others are existing in a life that is more like death.

Today, twenty years later, the names of Hiroshima and Nagasaki are more alive than they were in 1945 and will remain as a warning to all mankind of the still greater possible terrors that the people of the world must prevent.

PLATE 2. Leopold Infeld in Toronto.

I remember how, during the war, I had several dreams that kept being repeated. Here is one of them: somewhere in Krakow, in the Kazimierz district, I went alone by streetcar in the direction of the Wawel Castle. The buildings were destroyed, ruins lay about and in the distance there was a sort of hill. Another theme—I was in Poland and afraid of the Nazis, running away from them. Or another: murdered bodies, corpses . . . among which I suddenly found myself . . . I fled from torture, of which I was afraid. . . . After such dreams I woke up soaking wet.

I seriously considered the possibility that after a Nazi victory in Europe Hitler would attack the United States and Canada. I was glad to think that in that case my life would be in my own hands, that at any moment I could commit suicide with my family. A spark of hope arose in me only when the Nazis attacked the Soviet Union. At that time, Professor [Barker] Fairley and I began the Canadian-Soviet Friendship Society. The atmosphere in Canada had changed. The former antagonism had disappeared; everywhere people were talking about the fight put up by the courageous Red Army, about the great Stalin. Even the Canadian Prime Minister[9] took part in a large meeting at which the former U.S. Ambassador to the Soviet Union, Joseph Davies, was the chief speaker.

After 1945 relations between Canada and the Soviet Union changed completely, once again. The papers began to carry articles against the Soviet Union until finally in February of 1946 it was suddenly announced that sixteen people had been arrested as Russian spies. How had this come about?

The code clerk of the Soviet Embassy in Canada, Gouzenko, suddenly fell in love with Canadian democracy and to his lover—to this Canadian democracy—he brought a present of a number of coded documents. It appeared from them that there was a spy ring composed of sixteen people. They used aliases in their reports but he claimed that he knew their real names. These sixteen people turned out, for the most part, to be intellectuals—two university professors, several engineers—people who would never have been suspected. For the first time in a Commonwealth country people were sent to jail by purely administrative measures, without the court order required by the Magna Carta, the basis of British justice. More—the Royal Commission formed for the purpose published a report on the investigation, giving all the names and accusations as established facts before any trials had been held. Even after the cases were heard and the courts found some of the accused not guilty, the Commission Report was not withdrawn.[10]

Among those arrested I found the names of two people I knew well. I had no doubt they were innocent. One, a scientist who was a professor in a Canadian university, was also known in the United States. Not only I but other professors as well, including conservatives and members of the staffs of famous American universities, believed in his innocence and wanted to help him. However, he was suspended because of the accusation until the court found him innocent.[11] The second, also a scientist, even after he was found innocent could not find work in Canada and had to go to Europe.[12]

Progressive Canadians were up in arms. An organization was formed to help secure defence for the accused. However, there were not many who were willing to be active in the organization. Only eight people, including two professors—Fairley and me. We were both at once dubbed "fellow-travellers." This term, which at first meant those who followed the Communist Party line, later came to mean anyone who did not spend twenty-four hours a day fighting communism.

Our small group collected money (this was fairly easy) for lawyers and to buy space in the papers for explanations of the historical background and the violation of Canadian justice involved in these summary arrests.

After a full month of confinement, the accused were released to await trial. During the trials it became clear that half of them were innocent; the court found no evidence to substantiate the charges. The other half were sentenced to from one to five years in jail—and for actions proving to have quite ridiculous aims. The accused were charged with giving out information concerning chemical explosives. I was amazed that the Soviet Union would be interested in such information. It was still more surprising that the information had ever been a secret from our allies. How could one keep secrets in wartime that concerned chemical explosions? I could have understood if the secrets had been related to the atomic bomb. The whole thing proved a dud.

Later, one of the engineers who was sentenced to two years wrote me every month from prison, that is, every time he was allowed. I had never met him but he knew of my scientific work and asked me for books about physics and for a subject for him to work on. When he left jail he came to me with the work completed. He later published this paper on the theory of antennas, and it was much quoted.[13]

Late in 1946, Churchill delivered his famous "Fulton speech," which first employed the term "iron curtain." This was the official declaration of the cold war.

During the war the Canadian-Soviet Friendship Society held a congress at which I led the scientific session. One of the participants was Vilhjalmur Stefansson, famous Arctic explorer; another was Norbert Wiener, the inventor of cybernetics.

I had met Norbert Wiener when his daughter was a student in Toronto and he came to visit her. He was of my age, short, fat, round-faced, with eyes full of wonder at the external world and what happens in it—a world he saw through thick glasses. He was always ready to talk about himself. His father had been a professor of Russian at Harvard and, if I remember rightly, a Russian Jew. Norbert Wiener entered college when he was only fourteen or fifteen and he had his doctorate when he was nineteen.[14] Next he went to Göttingen, to that Mecca of mathematicians, for further study. Someone told me the following story about his stay there. A lecture he gave on his work was attended by [David] Hilbert, one of the greatest mathematicians of our century. After the seminar, all those present went, as was their weekly custom, to a beer cellar. Hilbert had asked only for beer and two rolls (no one dared order anything else) when [Felix] Klein appeared. Hilbert greeted him with:

"Professor, it's a shame you didn't attend today's seminar."

Wiener wondered: "Will he add something complimentary about the lecture?"

"We have had many interesting lectures of various kinds, better and worse, but such a bad lecture as today's we've never had before."

Another of the many stories that circulated about him was this: Once as he was walking on the M.I.T. campus he met one of his assistants and began to converse with him. As they talked they moved about. Before leaving, Wiener asked:

"Where exactly did we meet? In which direction was I heading?"

"Why do you ask?" enquired the puzzled assistant.

"Because only then can I know whether I was on the way to dinner or whether I've already had it."

Once we met at a scientific meeting in Boston and we talked and talked. He told me about a detective story he wanted to write in which no one would be able to guess the murderer. I only remember that it depended on a clever use of sleighs. We talked until three a.m. When, terribly tired, I left him, he asked me:

"Is there a meeting going on now that I ought to attend?"

I answered him:

"But it's three in the morning. We'll be meeting today at ten o'clock."

He then gave me the manuscript of his *Cybernetics* and asked me to read it.[15] I took it and when we met at nine for breakfast, he asked me whether I had finished it.

Once when Professor Wiener came to see me in Toronto, he talked rapidly about a book on philosophy that he was writing and about mathematical machines. He said then that it is possible for man to make a machine to which he would not himself be superior in any way. We asked him whether a machine could make up its own problems or plan new tasks. He said with certainty that it could, that a machine could set its own problems and solve them.

Once we invited him to lecture at the University of Toronto. The hall was full. I was a little late and had to sit in the last row where there was still a free place. Wiener came right up to that row and gave his speech into my ear, so that he could not be heard by the audience.

Another time his lecture made a great impression because it was semi-popular. He presented the idea of cybernetics, then a quite new science, in such a fascinating way that we asked him to repeat the lecture in a still more popular way and we invited doctors, engineers, and biologists. Wiener agreed but just before the lecture he told me:

"I'm going to talk about something else today."

He then began a highly mathematical lecture which could not be understood by a single doctor or biologist—and they had all been especially invited.

When he saw me once in Toronto after a long interval, he came to my room and his first words, even before shaking hands, were: "Planck's Law must be changed!"

He liked to talk in Chinese, a language he said he had learned during a one-year visit to China. And perhaps it really was Chinese!

He was undoubtedly a genius, but not in the same sense as Einstein whose genius was quiet, easy, and slow. Wiener's brain was on fire—everything burned in it, great and small. He should have had several assistants, especially to sort out the important ideas from the silly ones.

Basically, the Polish emigrés in Canada divided into two groups. The first was composed of progressives—communists and their sympathizers or non-party people who understood that the future of Poland was necessarily bound up with the Soviet Union. The second group, much larger, was made up of violent opponents of the Soviet Union. I had contact with the first of these and even gave some speeches for Canadian workers of Polish origin. (Recently I received a very pleasant and touching letter from one of them in Toronto who recalled my lecture, now, after twenty years!) I had little to do with the second group. I can only remember meeting two members of it. One had been the Polish consul in Germany and was living in Montreal. He came to Toronto from time to time to see me. He was quite interesting, intelligent, with some sense of humour but full of hatred towards the Soviet Union. He tried to convince me that the Polish army would make its way through the Balkans to Poland and establish a new force—a "third force" between Russia and Germany.

When I wrote to him in Montreal that I was considering signing the Appeal to Reason prepared by Oskar Lange, he came to see me to persuade me not to do so or at least to wait for a month. His argument had the effect of convincing me that I ought to sign at once.[16]

My experience with the second member of that persuasion, whom I met in Toronto, was less pleasant. He was Professor [Oscar] Halecki, the president of the Polish Academy in exile which included all Polish professors who were outside Poland during the war. When Mr. Halecki came to Toronto to give a lecture, the President of the University, Canon Cody, invited me to dinner with him. Cody was then close to retirement, a Conservative, a former minister of education of the Province of Ontario, and an honorary member of the Academy in Exile. He was easy-going, limited, and at an age when sclerosis begins. At dinner we had a rather stiff conversation and afterwards went to Professor Halecki's lecture. It was technically excellent but so full of hatred for the Soviet Union that I returned home depressed. At once I sent Halecki my resignation from the Academy he led, and I sent copies of my letter to the Canadian press.

At the same time I wrote an objective (or so it seemed to me) article about Poland for the literary monthly *Forum*.[17] In it I defended the Polish *raisons d'état*. (This was before the recognition of the People's Republic of Poland by the Canadian government.) A large part, though not all, of this article was reprinted by *Izvestia* and *Pravda* in the Soviet Union as well as by many Canadian publications.

Not long after the formation of the People's Republic of Poland, diplomatic relations were established between Poland and Canada. It so happened that I had to lecture in Ottawa on the atomic bomb at the time and made use of the opportunity to contact the Polish representative in Canada, Doctor [Alfred] Fiderkiewicz. The Ministry was located in two rooms in an Ottawa hotel which also served as the Minister's home. We had lunch together and he told me that the Polish treasures—Chrobry's mace, the Arras tapestries, and other priceless relics—were being held in Canada. At first I thought he was joking, but it turned out to be true. But now, as I write this in November 1963, the treasures have at last returned to Poland.

The entire staff of the Ministry turned out for my lecture, and the chairman publicly welcomed the Minister.

The next representative of Poland was Eugeniusz Milnikiel who later became Polish Ambassador in England and whom I still regard as a friend. Minister Milnikiel then proposed to me that I visit Poland for a few weeks. He invited me in the name of the government to lecture at Polish universities and at the same time advise the government on the organization of the study of physics in Poland.

The academic year in Canada is very short—it ends about the fifteenth of April so that, by the end of April, 1949, I could go to war-damaged Europe, for the first time in thirteen years.

I looked upon this trip as a four-week adventure after which I would return to Canada where I would finally be buried. In general I was fond of Canada. It was a plesasant and easy-going country; life there was peaceful, especially for a family with children. We lived in a house with a garden in a suburban district. Life was comfortable; a good school for our children Eric and Joan was close to home. Shopping was easy, much of it done by telephone. I did not dream that I might leave the country, my house and friends who grew in numbers with every passing year. What people there thought about my visit to Poland can best be explained by the comment of one of my colleagues:

"What? You're not afraid to go to Poland? But they won't let you out again!"

"Why?"

"Because you can be useful to them."

Inasmuch as I will have unpleasant things to relate about Canada, particularly about some of her high officials of the time, I must also speak of the good things. In this connection, I should like to tell my Polish readers how one obtained a passport in Canada. One went either to a bank or to a post office and took a blank. One filled it out. There were very few questions: "When were you born? Where? Are you a Canadian citizen?" There were no questions of the type used in Poland, like "Have you been abroad before?" and "Have you relatives abroad?" Then followed the statement: "Everything written here is true, which I affirm by my signature." The only other things necessary were a cheque for two dollars (the price of the passport) and photographs. These had to be verified either by a clergyman or a bank director. Why by just those? For such are the privileged ones in the country. Who verifies their photographs I don't know.

In five days I received a passport good for five years for all countries and, of course, for many trips. When I looked at it I discovered that instead of Leopold my first name appeared as Leo. I didn't want to go abroad with a document not in the right name, so I telephoned to the Department of Internal Affairs in Ottawa (I might add that the connection there is made at once, without putting down the receiver) and I told the clerk who answered that I wanted to change my passport. The person at the other end asked me to wait a moment and called the proper clerk. The latter was actually in her office and asked me to wait while she found my folder. After a minute she told me to return the old passport by express post and that I would receive a new one by express in three days. I was to leave on the fourth day. And, indeed, the morning post of the third day brought the new passport with the correct name. This small incident increased my attachment to Canada.

I flew to Ireland, invited by Professor Synge to lecture in Dublin. The Irish are charming talkers, and this country of drinkers and philosophers has an inexpressible charm. For me it was thrilling to have my first contact in many years with old Europe. I was to lecture at the Institute for Advanced Studies. Among the professors there at the time were [Erwin] Schroedinger, a Nobel prize winner (he died not long ago in Vienna), Professor Synge, of whom I have already written, [Walter] Heitler, now in Zurich, and [Lajos] Jánossy, today a professor in Hungary. I lectured about my work with Einstein on motion and relativity.

It is probably unthinkable that in Canada a scientific lecture would be attended by a premier or a national hero. But [Eamon] De Valera, President and national hero of Ireland, came to mine.

From Dublin I flew directly to London. Ambassador [Kazimierz] Michałowski and his wife were very hospitable. They arranged a dinner attended by—I remember it well—the Nobel prize-winner [Patrick Maynard Stuart] Blackett, Professor [John Desmond] Bernal, Professor [Léon] Rosenfeld from Manchester, Hyman Levy (professor at the University of London) and Antoni Słonimski— Polish poet and head of the Polish Cultural Centre—who organized the dinner. The atmosphere was relaxed and everyone envied me because I was going to Poland. They were interested in what my reaction would be to the changes I would find in the country.

When I was in England in 1933, I had a friend whom I then considered beautiful. She had a Gioconda smile and a husband who was a fourth-rate writer. He always boasted of the letters he had received from George Bernard Shaw. Now, when I returned to England after sixteen years, I wanted to see my old friend although I also feared the meeting after so long a time. I had not had any contact with her in recent years—not even by letter. No one answered the telephone. I rang up a mutual friend and learned that she had died three months before and her husband not long after. Depressed from this first unpleasant contact, I found London sad and poor, the people tired from the war and badly dressed. The food was never tasty in England—good raw materials spoiled in cooking. Now there were poor materials badly prepared.

After a three-day visit to London I flew in an English army plane to Poland through Berlin. In that city I spent one night and one day in the Polish Military Mission, in the English or perhaps French sector. It was during the "air lift" when all materials—coal, food, et cetera, were brought into Berlin by planes which landed every few minutes at Tempelhof. Food, light, and heat were used sparingly. Berlin seemed depressing. It was dark—light could be turned on only for two hours a day. Along Kurfürstendamm, trams moved among rubble, and grass grew between the tracks. In front of the Tiergarten women sold chocolate and themselves; dissipation was rife. The cafés were empty; among bare tables waiters moved in old frock coats. For a hundred packages of cigarettes one could buy a grand piano. And from this poverty the unscrupulous made fortunes. Many prostitutes solicited among the demoralized soldiers of the Allied armies.

From Berlin I flew to Poland—to Warsaw—with mixed feelings. Poland was the place where my family had perished in Nazi camps—I did not even know where. It was the place where my younger sister had died—my best and beloved friend, whose charm and goodness have not been forgotten by any who knew her. On the other hand, I was aware that the social system was now much closer to me than that which had obtained between the two world wars.

At the airport I was awaited by Mr. [Włodzimierz] Michajłow who, I learned later, was the director of the Research Section of the Ministry of Education. With him was Karol Majewski, assistant to the professor of theoretical physics in Warsaw.

We drove through streets on which alternated ruins and one-story buildings. As we passed down a broad, rubble-filled street I asked its name and learned that it was Marszałkowska Street, formerly one of the busiest thoroughfares. We turned on Nowy Świat Street, already partly reconstructed, but the buildings still without facing. At the Bristol Hotel, where I was to stay, I had a chat with Director Michajłow and Mr. Majewski. They told me briefly about the state of theoretical physics in Poland, which proved to be very bad. In Warsaw there were two theoretical physicists—Professor [Czeslaw] Białobrzeski, an older man, and Professor [Wojciech] Rubinowicz, the only one in Poland who had a reputation beyond the borders of the country. In Krakow there was Professor [Jan] Weyssenhoff, sixty years old, who, they said, was then studying in Switzerland. In Poznań was Professor [Szczepan] Szczeniowski, my former department head, previously professor at Vilna: he was about fifty years old. Only in

Toruń were there two younger men who had emerged since the war
and whose names I knew from their papers.[18]

That same day I went to see Julian Tuwim. He had returned to
Poland several years before. On his door was a sign reading something
like this: "No one, but no one, will be admitted under any condition
without a previous appointment made by telephone. My number is
..." I wondered whether to enter or to return six floors down and
telephone. I decided to try my luck and ring the bell. A nurse opened.
When I asked whether I could come in, she let me enter without
protest. I walked straight into a room full of people since no one seemed
to be ready to announce me. Tuwim, looking badly and much thinner,
was sitting with his back to me so that he did not see me. The people
around him were talking about his stomach operation and the fact that
he must watch his diet. No one noticed my presence. Suddenly Tuwim
turned and had a shock, thinking that he was seeing a ghost from
Canada.

One reason for my visit to Tuwim was to ask for the address of
Wikta. She was my old friend—one of the few from the past who was
still alive. I remembered her from twenty years before as a beautiful
girl, exceptionally intelligent—I would guess the most intelligent
and clever woman in Poland, admired by me and all the men who
knew her. I phoned her and we met. Her beauty and youth had
gone but her intelligence and wit remained. Wikta was my mentor
during my stay in Poland, helping me to know and understand the
country.

I lectured in Warsaw, Krakow, and Wrocław. Warsaw was very
vivid although it then had only a few hundred thousand inhabitants.
As a city it was still dead, but its inhabitants were very much alive.
The women were quite well dressed, more as a result of ingenuity
than money. When I said that I couldn't understand where the people
seen on the streets lived, I was told: "Oh, but you should have seen
this city four years ago! Then there were only heaps of rubble over
which it was impossible to walk. You wouldn't have seen any streets;
there were no tracks—only stones and more stones. The hundred
thousand people then lived mostly in Praga (on the other bank of the
river). The whole government was there in one building. Even the key
to the toilet was kept by the premier and anyone who wanted to use
it had first to knock on the premier's door."

It gave me great pleasure to go to Krakow, a city without ruins, neglected but beautiful, though now foreign to me. I saw no one there of the many I had known as a young man.

I also lectured in Wrocław. It seemed ugly, composed of alien ruins. The older professors received me with some reserve—polite, proper, but without friendliness. However, the young people came to me eagerly.

In general I was better received by the officials of the Ministry of Education than by academic circles. Among those of the older generation who were very pleasant to me was Professor [Stefan] Pieńkowski who had done much for experimental physics, particularly in the years between the two world wars. Still very vigorous, somewhat dictatorial, he was a fine organizer, very intelligent, and he had great charm.

Many things in Poland were not to my taste. First of all I was disturbed by the attitude of suspicion towards people from the West. Then there was the poor standard of living and the low level of science —even lower than in Canada. But many things pleased me. First I would put the intelligence of the people, their liveliness and sense of humour. Though this sense of humour was not a simple thing—it was usually lost when the person got up on a platform.

But life had prepared me to be sympathetic to socialism, to make allowances for the lacks I observed, to remember mainly the good things. In brief, despite the flaws I observed and those I did not realize, I loved this Poland. I was sorry when my visit ended and it was difficult for me to leave the country. I regretted that I would no longer hear Wikta's laughter or my native language, that I would no longer see this poor country with all its ruins. Therefore I rejoiced when Vice-Minister of Education Krassowska proposed that I return. What most drew me to the country was the great dynamics of its recovery. I realized that tomorrow would probably be better. Yet I felt too old to give up the comforts that awaited me in Canada. Thus I suggested a compromise. I was due for a sabbatical leave. I realized that the following year I must spend in Toronto. But I proposed that after that, for the next academic year, I would come to Poland. It was a consolation to know that I would see the country once again.

Before I left I wrote a lengthy report on the state of physics in Poland and how to improve it. It contained many extremely clever ideas on the future of physics in Poland, which, as far as I know, no one ever read or applied.

Why I Left Canada

As I write these words it is November of 1963. My wife and I recall
the year 1949–50 which we spent in Canada. I have dug out the newspaper file—a pile of clippings accumulated fourteen years ago. They
are from Sydney, Australia, from New Zealand, from China, from
Paris, London, and various American cities, from the smallest towns
in Canada. They are clippings in which my name appears. That sad
fame quickly died out, only to flare up again after a few months. I
write these words with a tension and nervousness that I want to cure
by setting them down on paper.

That year was undoubtedly the saddest of my life. Halina's death
had been a great tragedy, but then I was twenty years younger and
had great vital force.[1] I could struggle against it and bear misfortune.
But in 1950 I was already fifty-two.

Let me begin at the beginning. All that I am about to write is
true as I saw it, as I now feel it. I will write everything, withholding
nothing. If I were religious I would say, "So help me God."

I returned from my short visit to Poland for a week in England in order to deliver a lecture in Manchester and one in Birmingham, as I was invited to do. Then I went straight to Toronto. It was either the end of May or the beginning of June. I told my wife about my adventures in Poland. As far as I remember, I told no one else because no one else was interested. If I began to talk about Poland, someone changed the subject. I wrote three articles for *Scientific American*— one on my visit to Dublin, one on my visit to England, and one on my visit to Poland.[2]

Yesterday I talked with my wife Helen about my return from Poland to Canada. She told me that after I came back I changed my attitude to the country. I myself recall how the wealth of Canada upset me—the rich but tasteless buildings, the people who had no idea what was happening in Europe, who did not appreciate scientific work —all this upset me and depressed me more and more. After I had returned I asked Helen whether she and the children would agree to come with me to Poland for a year. I told her I knew it would be difficult, that we would miss the comfort that we had in Canada, and that we would return after the year was over. Yesterday my wife admitted that she had agreed rather unwillingly. She feared the diffi- culties that would be created by her not knowing the language and also by the poverty there. These difficulties worried her especially in connection with the children, who were then ten and six. Still, I felt that the Polish government would help us, and that the year would not be too difficult. I was very eager to go, if only for a short time.

Before making up my mind, I wanted to find out what Einstein thought about it. Therefore, we went to visit Helen's parents in New Jersey near New York, and from there I drove with my whole family to Princeton. Then, for the first time in ten years, I saw again that good and well-known house that figured in so many of my memories. I had a feeling that I was seeing Einstein for the last time. I asked Helen and the children to go for a walk for an hour as I wanted to talk first with Einstein by myself. We discussed scientific matters. He told me of his work with the enthusiasm he always reserved for his latest ideas. I asked him what he thought of my plan to go to Poland for a year. He answered quietly that it was very good of me to wish to go, that no one should have anything against it. He was only afraid that things might become worse in Poland and asked me whether

I had allowed for that. I was not afraid of it and took Einstein's comment to mean approval.

Before I wrote these words I asked my son whether he remembered the visit. He said he did. But when it came to a description of what he recalled, he was very vague. He said that Einstein laughed loudly at some political jokes I had brought back from Europe, that his sister had given the children some chocolate bars. My son kept his for some time in the icebox and said he would never eat it but keep it as a memento. However, later he and his sister did eat their chocolate. I remember that, before saying goodbye, Einstein remarked that he liked my children very much.

As we drove back through New Jersey and saw the lovely, well-cared-for houses, in such good condition, I pictured America to myself as a bag bursting with gold. And how distasteful I found it! This was something I had never felt before, a proof of the profound impression Poland had made on me.

We returned to Toronto and planned our trip to Vancouver, where I was to take part in a high-level four-week course in theoretical physics. Among the lecturers were to be P[aul] A[drien] M[aurice] Dirac and Homi Bhabha, and I was to conduct a seminar twice a week on theoretical physics.

On the way to Vancouver we made a two-week stop-over at Banff in the Rocky Mountains. I do not feel at ease in high mountains—they overpower me and make me feel foolish, climbing them to look back at the place from which I started. Besides, my weak heart prevents me from moving about much at such heights and I must remain rather inactive. Still, the two weeks in Banff were very pleasant. Bears roam nearby, and on the streets of the town can be seen deer and other wild animals that neither attack nor fear man.

The probability of meeting a physicist in Banff is very small. So I was quite surprised when, on the street, I ran into Dirac. I had known him in England years earlier and again more recently during a visit to Toronto. I knew he was a silent type who answered questions with either "yes" or "no." But in Banff he was more talkative. He had spent two weeks away from people and had not spoken a word, thus accumulating a collection of phrases that he suddenly released on me. Despite his natural reluctance to talk—or perhaps because of it—he is intelligent and deep, and never utters a triviality.

Later we went to Vancouver. In the western part of Canada the people are different—more lively, more imaginative than in the east. The university had rather primitive buildings. Only the physics building was attractive. The surroundings, however, were breathtakingly beautiful with a view of the mountains and the sea. Vancouver lies in a lovely spot—as magnificent as the Bay of Naples, if not more so.

At that time the Canadian Mathematical Association organized a course in mathematics and theoretical physics given every two years, and for this purpose collected money from bankers, philanthropists and other wealthy people. Most of the work was done by Professor [W. L. G.] Williams of Montreal who was in charge of finances. Once I went along with him on one of his visits to a prospective donor. I was interested to see how he did it. He talked about the general needs of science and made no particular appeal. I thought it was wasted time and said:

"Nothing came of that visit."

He replied, "No matter, no matter. They must be prepared slowly, must get used to the idea that they have to give some money."

At the University of British Columbia in Vancouver, theoretical physics was well represented, but there was no graduate course and no Ph.D.s were granted. The leading physicist was Professor [George Michael] Volkoff. Then young, an excellent lecturer, born in Russia, intensely opposed to the Soviet Union, he had left the country as a young boy during the revolution. He was happy to tell me that my book with Einstein, *The Evolution of Physics*, had been criticized in the USSR. He gave me a translation of the review he had prepared for me. In this way I learned that Einstein and I were wrong, that the book was "idealistic," and that it had been a mistake to translate it into Russian.

The Vancouver staff also had a Pole, Professor Opechowski. When I told him about my desire to visit Poland he revealed sympathy for the country but said that he had no national feeling, that he was happy in Canada. As a physicist, Professor Opechowski was more critical than creative. The department also contained two Germans. One of them was pleasant and, I think, liberal. The second seemed less so; he wanted to return to Germany and I believe he later did. Thus the department consisted of two Germans, one Pole, one Russian and not one native Canadian.[3] Practically all the students at the course were my products from the University of Toronto, and it was a great pleasure for me to meet with my former and present students once again.

Homi Bhabha, a handsome and well-dressed professor from India whom I met at Vancouver, was a very capable and well-known physicist. Today, he is more a representative of physics than a physicist. I also became acquainted with another Pole—Antoni Zygmund —who was a professor at the University of Chicago and also an invited lecturer. Then there was Professor Schwartz of Paris who talked on the delta-function (so important for theoretical physics), of which he was the first to give an exact theory. His lectures were especially beautiful. In politics he was known as a Trotskyite. Recently, in Poland, I read in the paper that he spoke on behalf of the Algerians' struggle for independence and lost his position.[4]

Soon after we returned to Toronto the new academic year began. Unexpectedly I received an invitation from Professor Eugene Wigner in Princeton, who was later to win a Nobel Prize. He asked me to Princeton for the second half of the academic year 1949–50 to lecture on the theory of relativity. Not only was this a desirable offer from the financial point of view, but also it represented the possibility of working with Einstein again. Of course, if I went to Princeton I could not then take another leave of absence to go to Poland—I realized this quite well. But I thought that it would even be worth while to risk the Polish visit for the opportunity to be in Princeton. Such visits to other universities were common in Toronto. My colleagues in the mathematics section of the department, especially professors [Harold Scott MacDonald] Coxeter and [Richard Dagobert] Brauer, went away every two or three years, taking unpaid leaves. I, on the other hand, in the twelve years spent in Canada, had not taken a single leave, paid or unpaid.

When I asked Dean Beatty, the head of the department, whether he would agree to my going, he replied that he would give me an answer in a few days. After the few days had passed it turned out that he refused outright because I had students and I was necessary to the university—I had undertaken to be in Toronto for the whole year and had to remain at least until the middle of April, the end of the academic year. Only then could I go to Princeton.

In that case, I told him, I asked for a leave the next year when I wished to visit several countries, including Poland. I thought that, using Poland as a centre, I could go to Copenhagen, Cambridge, and Zurich, where [Wolfgang] Pauli was, for a few months each. I thought this plan would make it easier for me to go abroad, that the administration would then more readily agree to my going to Poland if I mentioned it together with other countries whose names sounded less dangerous to Canadian ears.

Professor Beatty told me that he saw no objection and that he would do all he could to persuade the president to agree to this proposal. I would have a leave, in his opinion even a paid leave, for the whole year.

After I handed in my official request, I learned from Dean Beatty that he had warmly supported it and that he was convinced that the president would not oppose it. After some time he told me that the president did agree to my trip, that I would certainly obtain a leave the next year, and that the final approval would be given by the Board of Governors of the university. He said this was a mere formality but that it would be done only in April. Thus I was convinced that I would go to Poland and I wrote an official letter—I don't remember to whom, whether to Mr. Michajłow or directly to the minister— saying that I accepted the invitation to Poland.

I did not feel well in Toronto and waited impatiently for the end of the academic year. My wife remembers that, at that time, I talked badly about my colleagues, that I was annoyed by every little thing. My scientific work did not go very well, either. One of my former students, who was then an assistant professor at the University of Toronto, left me for a much better position in the United States. I felt lonely. I waited only for the end of the term. I thought that, in April or May, I would leave for the year in Poland; lectures ended in Toronto at the beginning of April, followed only by exams which I could ask a colleague to mark. I had done the same when I left for Europe in 1949.

In order that what later happened can be understood, I quote here from the conclusion of a long article about my book *Quest*, which appeared in the Toronto *Globe and Mail* six years before, in 1944:

"'But,' he says thoughtfully, 'a progressive government in a new Poland that needs him would attract him back to Europe.'"

Why I Left Canada

March is a sad month in Toronto. The sky is overcast, rain pours down and, although winter has ended, spring is far away. On such a day a colleague of mine, a professor of mathematics, telephoned to me to ask whether I could still find time that day for an editor who wanted to talk to me. I often gave interviews and, since my colleague requested it, I did not even ask what paper he came from. I agreed at once. A certain Mr. Thompson then came to me and introduced himself as an editor of *The Ensign*. Later I learned that this was a weekly published in Montreal. Mr. Thompson told me that he had been an editor of *Newsweek*. I wondered why he had now become editor of an unimportant Canadian publication. I gave him the interview, since I had nothing to hide. I also gave him my three articles from *Scientific American* in which I had written about my trip. I told him that I had put in a request for a leave to visit several countries next year and that Professor Beatty had assured me that I would be granted it, and also that I had liked Poland very much in general. That was all.

Mr. Thompson did not impress me very pleasantly. There was something sly about him. He pretended to like me and even asked me to write an article for *The Ensign*.

Suddenly, in the beginning of March, I received a telephone call from the United Press or the Associated Press, I don't remember which, I heard the voice say:

"In two days *The Ensign* will appear with a long article about you. Do you know about it?"

"No."

"In that case I'll read the article to you because I'd like to know what you think of it."

The title of the article was "Professor Infeld Recalled to Poland" and it said something like this (unfortunately I so disliked the publication that I have not kept a copy). In ten pages (with various photographs of me) the author discussed my case—saying that I was a well-known authority on atomic science, that I learned atomic secrets from Einstein, that I wanted to give these atomic secrets to Russia by way of Poland, that (as every reader could easily conclude) I was a traitor to Canada, and that Canada should do everything possible so that I would not be able to take this trip.

I listened nervously, red with anger and shame, to the words coming smoothly over the telephone wire. I told the man at the other end

45

that it was all completely untrue. I couldn't say more because I felt as though I were being strangled.

I quote here an excerpt from an article on this affair in a paper [*British Columbian*] of 15 March 1950 that appeared in the small town of New Westminster in the distant province of British Columbia.

CANADIAN SCIENTIST ANGERED BY PRESS

Toronto, March 15—A Catholic newspaper was charged with scandalous and false reporting today by a naturalized Canadian whom it said was being "recalled" by the Polish communists to teach about atomic energy.

Dr. Infeld, 51, one of the world's leading mathematicians and a former associate of Prof. Albert Einstein, said a report about him in the Montreal-published weekly *The Ensign* was "utterly fantastic, untrue, and unbelievable. It's a scandal."

The newspaper said Infeld, "a recognized authority on theoretical aspects of atomic energy, is planning to return to communist Poland to study and teach at Warsaw University."

"He is thoroughly familiar with the theory and much of the practical applications of atomic energy," the paper said in a Toronto dispatch. . . .

"I have been a citizen of Canada for ten years," he said. "No country can recall me. I have never been an atomic scientist and never had anything to do with atomic research. I have no secrets."

It appeared that *The Ensign* was a weekly, little known and little read—that it was a Catholic sheet sold in front of churches. Yet it was the source of the waves of persecution that quickly rose around me.

Journalists immediately approached President Smith who had succeeded Canon Cody and asked whether I had really obtained a leave of absence. He avoided a straight answer as well as he could, in proof of which I give part of an article from the Toronto *Telegram* of 18 March. The complete article is over twice as long as the quote.

LEAVE FROM VARSITY SOUGHT BY INFELD

Though Dr. Leopold Infeld, University of Toronto mathematics professor, has made application for leave of absence to his immediate superior—the head of the mathematics department, it has not yet been officially received by the president of the University, Dr. Sidney Smith said today.

"There is nothing fishy or sinister in that," said Dr. Smith. "Applications for leave of absence, of which there are several every year, are to be considered at the April meeting of the university's Board of Governors."

I was afraid that the affair was being whipped up, and that I would not be able to visit Poland. But I still hoped that, after my categorical statement that I had nothing to do with the atomic bomb, the affair would die down. I thought that people would forget about the whole thing and that, slowly, everything would return to normal.

Here I must recall the nature of the political parties then in Canada. There were five, but only two of them had ever formed a government. One was the Liberal Party, led during the war by Mackenzie King, the former prime minister. The second was the Conservative Party which had changed its name to Progressive-Conservative and was led by George Drew.

I did not know Drew, though we had once shared the gentlemen's room at the airport in Ottawa. However, my wife had had a disagreement with him when, as Premier of Ontario, he introduced religious education into the schools. A committee of citizens was formed to defend the schools' secular nature and it even included clergymen. Once Drew deigned to receive a delegation to present the committee's position; my wife was a member. She told me how Drew had criticized the committee on the basis that its members were not Canadians. Being an American citizen, she told him sharply that he undoubtedly was thinking of her, but that, as the mother of two children who were born in Canada, she felt that it was not only her right but her duty to interest herself in their education. Apparently, Drew turned red and began to apologize. He was unusually handsome and was referred to as "gorgeous George," but he was a poor politician. Today he plays no role at all.

To return to my story. One evening at nine o'clock the telephone rang, this time from Ottawa. An unknown voice told me that Drew had brought up my affair in Parliament. It is the custom in Canada that important international affairs threatening the safety of Canada can be interpolated into the debate even if not on the agenda.

Apparently Drew looked upon my trip to Poland as a matter threatening the safety of the country.

I put down the receiver in a state of semi-consciousness. Helen asked what had happened, why I was so pale. I only answered: "We're being hounded." That night we could not sleep. We waited for the morning *Globe and Mail*. Here is a part of its long article of 16 March.

Ottawa, March 16—Progressive Conservative Leader George Drew told the House of Commons today it would be remarkable if a professor were able to draw half pay from the University of Toronto while organizing educational activities in Poland under the aegis of the Communists. . . .

In Toronto, Dr. Infeld said he was sorry to hear Mr. Drew was misled by the article in the *Ensign*.

The reports were "utterly untrue" he said. . . .

The tenor of the Opposition Leader's speech was that the Toronto professor should not be allowed to return behind the Iron Curtain with atomic information. . . .

Mr. Drew suggested the appropriate department of the government look into the matter.

"Having regard to what has already happened under similar circumstances, appropriate steps should be taken to ascertain the circumstances under which Dr. Infeld plans to return to Poland armed with certain atomic knowledge that he gained during two years' association with Dr. Einstein in the United States and from several years' activity in the fields of mathematics and physics at the University of Toronto," Mr. Drew said.

Mr. Drew indicated he had other information besides the *Ensign* article.

"It is stated in the article, and I have other evidence to the same effect, that in 1946 he predicted that Russia would have the atomic bomb in three years," said Mr. Drew.

"It was a strangely accurate prediction. It also is disclosed, and this does not surprise me, that this scientist, who was a refugee from Poland and was welcome as a professor at the University of Toronto, was teaching in Warsaw and Krakow last summer."

"Everyone knew," said Mr. Drew, "that in Communist countries education had to conform to more than academic standards. Those engaged as teachers were subject to qualifications which did not relate to their academic standing and were under certain limitations."

I felt isolated; the state machine was against me. It would be impossible now to go to the United States; I wouldn't be allowed to cross the "border of peace and friendship." This would mean scientific isolation. If I was regarded as a potential traitor to Canada, would I be able to keep my position?

I was convinced that the reason for these attacks was my political outlook. I was ashamed to show my face. I remember that it was a rainy day when the news of Drew's interpolation became known. I had to go to my lecture and before that to the bank. I remember how I walked through the rain—unhappy and depressed. On the way I saw discarded copies of the *Globe and Mail* carrying the article and my picture on the first page, crumpled and trampled upon. I went to the bank to cash a check. I remember that the cashier looked at me queerly. Usually I passed the time of day with him, but not then. Later at my lecture I was embarrassed to face my students. I imagined that they all looked on me as a spy, believing that I wanted to sell Canada and take away the secret of the atomic bomb.

At home the telephone rang constantly—journalists sought interviews. I selected one, a representative of the Associated Press, since his voice on the telephone seemed less insistent than the others. I remember that there was a blizzard on the day the reporter came and asked me questions, mostly about my supposed part in atomic experiments. He wrote a good article, an objective one. He did not hide his personal sympathy for me. I thought Drew would be influenced by the truth and would withdraw his attack. But what was that politician's reaction? He merely said that I had not told the truth.

Many articles appeared on this affair in various publications and even drew in Einstein. His secretary wrote me in March 1950:

> Thanks for your letter. We had a telephone call last week from the Associated Press. I was so amazed that I nearly lost my temper. I shouted into the telephone "utter nonsense." Prof. E. said afterwards that this was the only appropriate comment. Please do not let things get you down. Your M.P. wanted to emulate Rankin,[5] I suppose. Your statement is very good and forthright.
>
> Once more: keep your equilibrium. *In 50 Jahren ist alles vorbei!*
> Regards from the whole family to you and yours,
>
> Helen D[ukas]

A national discussion developed. For all I know it may have been worldwide. As examples, I quote from an article for me and one against me. The most vulgar, the worst was the one I quote from only in part, since its ending does not concern me but other people, also slandered.

The *Ensign*, 1 April 1950:

MORE ON DR. INFELD

A Communist regime was established in Poland some four years ago. Its ferocity of persecution, suppression of free learning and abject sub-servience to Soviet imperialism are a matter of dismal record.

Travel in Poland has been restricted, and teaching regimented. Out-side of an ever smaller number of foreign correspondents, only those "politically reliable" from the communist point of view are readily granted visas and permitted to enter. This unfortunately is also a matter of record.

So the *Ensign* saw it as a matter of duty and urgent public interest to draw attention to the fact that an eminent physio-mathematician from the University of Toronto, Dr. Leopold Infeld, had been invited to lecture at the communist-controlled Polish universities last year and now planned to return there this year for further teaching. Immediately, Dr. Infeld, in a statement to the press, said, the *Ensign*'s story was "utterly untrue," despite the fact that he had himself told the *Ensign* of his plans.

Then the Hon. George Drew brought the matter to the attention of the House of Commons.

On Friday, after three days of vigorous denials, Dr. Infeld admitted to the Canadian Press in an interview: "I told my superior at the University about two months ago that I would like a year's leave of absence. . . . I did and do intend when I'm there to give some graduate lectures at the University of Warsaw and to work with those who are interested in the same field of research."

Dr. Infeld also protested that he knew nothing of atomic matters, but this cannot be taken very seriously. It is too well established that the whole realm of nuclear physics is largely based on the mathematical dis-coveries of men like Einstein and other leading physio-mathematicians. There can be little argument but that without such discoveries in higher mathematics the purely mechanical "know-how" of atomic production would never have been possible. On what authority—except his scientific achievements—did Dr. Infeld engage in frequent public discussions of the atomic bomb, the level of Soviet research and related phases of nuclear science? In his new book *Albert Einstein* (Saunders-Toronto),[6] he makes it clear that no atom bomb would have been possible without mathematical research as a pre-requisite.

Physio-mathematics have for some years been of great benefit to many applied scientific fields. During the war Dr. Infeld himself worked on radar for the National Research Council.

But there are other reasons for the concern the *Ensign* feels about these goings and comings of the Toronto professor to and from universities in communist Warsaw and Krakow. . . .

In such circumstances it became a dictate of duty for the *Ensign* to bring this matter to the level of the public record.

We did. Canadians now know the facts.

Among publications that can be regarded as political there were also some that carried articles in my defence. Here is an abbreviated version of an article from the serious Ottawa [Evening] *Citizen* [18 March 1950]:

It's not likely, at this stage, that the Board of Governors of the University of Toronto will accept any long-distance instruction in their duties from Mr. George Drew in Ottawa. Nor is it likely that the federal government, as he has suggested, would look into the circumstances of Dr. Infeld's plans to return to Poland "with certain atomic knowledge." Nor is it likely that anyone is going to prevent Dr. Infeld from going to Poland, if he wants to. It seems that Mr. Drew had nothing to go on, except an article in the *Ensign*, the Roman Catholic weekly that has become hysterical over the cold war. . . . Mr. Drew, however, has left the insinuation that Dr. Infeld has had something to do with the fact the Russians now have the atomic bomb, having made "a strangely accurate prediction" in 1946, and that the Toronto scientist intends to convey atomic information to the Polish government.

The propriety of Mr. Drew's remarks may be judged by Dr. Infeld's known views. Dr. Infeld was born in Poland, educated at Krakow, Cambridge and Princeton universities. Now a professor of mathematics at Toronto, he is an outstanding authority in the field of experimental [*sic*] physics and a collaborator with Albert Einstein on the general relativity theory. Einstein and he wrote a book on "The Evolution of Physics" in 1938. Infeld is one of a rather rare species, an articulate scientist who can write lucidly about science. His book *Quest, The Evolution of a Scientist* (1941), is a notable autobiography. It won a literary award. He is not, however, an "atomic scientist," having had nothing to do with the practical development of atomic energy. It is a fair inference, however, that he could explain the atomic bomb, or the hydrogen bomb for that matter, as well as anyone in the world.

Dr. Infeld wrote in 1946 a pamphlet, "Atomic Energy and World Government," for the Canadian Institute of International Affairs, a nonpolitical organization of unimpeachable standing. His guess was that "at the beginning of 1948" the Soviet Union and even France and Sweden "may" be making atomic bombs. The sinister implication given to this by Mr. Drew needs to be weighed against the fact that Dr. Infeld, of all people, knows enough atomic theory to give an informed guess of the time needed to get into production of A-bombs. To judge his guess, the relevant date is Sept. 22, 1949, when President Truman announced that the Russians had set off an atomic explosion. Dr. Infeld was rather far off base. But the point he was making in 1946 was that atomic policy based on secrecy and the assumption that the A-bomb would remain a monopoly, would lead to an impass of fear and mistrust.

A number of people came to see me to persuade me to give up my trip, to stay in Canada or to go anywhere else, only not to Poland. They were mainly conservatives who were my friends, whom I respected, and who wished me well. They told me that I was a victim, that there were many more victims in the United States—for example Lattimore[7] —who were attacked by various congressional committees for years and who were also not guilty.

I well remember the visit of William Deacon, an older man, very friendly to me. He was the literary editor of the *Globe and Mail* and had liked my books.[8] He came to me with his wife and told me that I was like a person who places himself in front of a tramway, that he wanted to defend me, to save me for Canada and he advised me to go anywhere at all for the year, but not to Poland.

I learned that an editor of the Ottawa *Citizen* was in town—the one who had written the rather favourable article about my affair. I invited him to come to see me. He was intelligent, pleasant, but full of poison about communism. He said to me—I shall never forget it—that if a communist were bleeding to death in front of his house, he would not open the door to him.

All these talks and discussions produced in me an increasing distaste for Canada, and pushed me towards Poland. For I thought not one of the people who would come to my hotel room in Poland would talk like this about even their worst enemies.

I had several very unpleasant talks with the president of the university. Sidney Smith was a good deal younger than his predecessor Canon Cody. He had been a lecturer in a non-university law school and had come to Toronto after serving as president of the University of Manitoba in Winnipeg. He was plump, rather good-looking, a Rotary club type. By this I mean that he could talk well, had a smile for everyone, remembered names, could flatter, but could also be sharp and vulgar. He was a pillar of the Conservative Party. (After I left Canada he became Minister of External Affairs. By the way, I heard while in Poland, and from a reliable source, that he was a poor minister. He died a few years ago.) I had many talks with him and Dean Beatty. In one of these, the President told me that he would offer me twice my salary not to go to Poland. He imagined that for a few thousand dollars he could buy me. Finally he told me that, though it would be a loss if I were to go on leave, or even stay away for good, the university would not collapse.

Most of those who talked to me, as I have said, were conservatives and suggested that I not go to Poland. Others thought I should go, among them "fellow travellers," who believed that Poland was the country of the future and that Canada, a capitalist country, was the dying world, the world of the past.

Unexpectedly, the Polish Minister in Ottawa, E. Milnikiel, came to see me. I felt as though a breath of fresh air had entered the room. He did not try to convince me to go to Poland but said that the decision was up to me, that he had telegraphed home about the attacks on me. He asked if he could help me in any way if I did decide to leave for Poland. I told him I intended to go although it now looked as though it might have to be forever. I added that I would like to have the invitation not only from the Ministry of Education but also from the rector of the University of Warsaw. He promised me that I would have it in a few days.

After this short visit I felt much better. I told all my friends that I could no longer bear the pressure, that I must decide for myself about my future. I asked them not to discuss my trip with me any more. I waited for the end of the academic year and the exams, after which I had decided to leave at once. I told my colleagues that I was going to England in order to consider the whole affair in peace and quiet. My wife agreed that she would take the children to New York and sail for Poland on the *Batory* in July. I had no idea what a burden I was placing on her—to prepare the house for our tenants (we had rented it to a friend), pack our things, arrange everything, and travel with two children, not knowing whether she would have unpleasantness at the border. On the other hand, I thought that as an American citizen nothing could happen to her. In any case she could go to New York and there obtain her Polish visa.

Thus in the middle of May I left Canada. I went first to London but even there I was afraid to take a Polish visa. I did not know whether the British authorities would allow me to board the *Batory* on which I was to sail to Poland. I had the impression that I was being followed. When the British officials asked me where I was going I said that I was going to Copenhagen, for which as a Canadian citizen I did not need a visa. Minister Milnikiel was on the ship, too, as he had been transferred to Sweden. During the journey Milnikiel told me about the arrests in Warsaw. I was convinced that these people were guilty. After all, I was familiar with the history of the French Revolution, and I knew how many traitors there had been to it, even among its heroes. (For example, Danton took the King's gold.) I couldn't believe that anyone could be persecuted or imprisoned illegally in Poland. Had I had any idea what was really happening during the Stalin period, which I learned only after the Twentieth Congress, I would not have gone to Poland.

When we arrived in Gdynia, I was greeted by Majewski, the same who had greeted me on my first arrival in the country. From Gdynia I went on to Warsaw. The cares of Toronto seemed far away.

Poland

And so I returned to Poland. Here I felt like a man on a trapeze, swinging up, down, and up again. I shall explain why a little later. First I should like to return to the Canadian affair.

No one in Canada knew that I was already in Poland. I had given my London address and mail was now forwarded from there. In this way I received a letter from Dean Beatty. He wrote that I must return for the beginning of the academic year. If not I would lose my wonderful job. To this I sent an answer which I do not quote in its entirety. I reiterated my relation to Toronto and Canada. The letter said in part:

> During my twelve years in Canada, the University was most generous to me. This I shall always remember with gratitude. When I left Poland in 1936 because there was no place under the old regime for me as a scientist, I was made welcome in Canada, which became the country of my adoption. Some of its hospitality I have tried to repay by doing

volunteer work during the recent war against fascism and later by my public lectures across the breadth of Canada on the basic issues of war and peace. The cordiality of my audiences convinced me that the Canadian people sincerely desire peace. In this, and in all my other activities I have tried to contribute my best to Canada.

Nevertheless, in the last months before I left, an organized campaign against me served to balk these efforts. As you well know, I was attacked with ignorant viciousness on a level to which I refused to descend even by way of reply. I was attacked publicly from the highest tribunal, and my motives for returning to visit Poland were slandered. The campaign of persecution, directed not only against me but also my wife, succeeded to this extent: that it made it impossible for me to carry on any further work in Canada. . . .[1]

Since, now, the University of Toronto forces me to make a choice, under threat of dismissal if I stay here for the year, my decision is to remain in my native land, to contribute all I can to the scholarship being done here. . . .[2]

Please, therefore, consider this letter to be my resignation from the position of Professor of Applied Mathematics at the University of Toronto.

Yours truly,
Leopold Infeld.

I must admit that certain accents in this letter are a bit artificial, but I really felt what I wrote.

About this time, a term was invented in America for the alteration of views by some sort of intensive indoctrination—"brainwashing." Judging from my own experience, this term really refers to something more tenuous, to the pressure of environment. I was then convinced that I was in my proper place, that Poland was the best of all countries —and today I am still convinced that I personally did the right thing in leaving Canada. Poland gave me the chance to build an institute. Fortunately for me, I was not aware of the grimness of the Stalinist times through which I lived.

My sense, the first time I visited Poland, of the opportunities for developing science proved to be true. I was given a place to work, I was flattered; life was made easy for me. I became convinced, to alter a known proverb, that no one is a prophet except in his own country.

My affair was publicized. I received copies of the Canadian papers with front page articles about my "disloyalty" to Canada. The news that I had decided to stay in Poland came out in the afternoon, and so the Toronto evening papers were filled with the story. Next day the news was old in North America and was given smaller space with smaller headlines.

I quote from an article in the more serious Canadian morning paper, the *Globe and Mail* [22 September 1950], signed by a certain Lex Schrag.

MATHEMATICIAN HARD TO FIGURE

Prof. Infeld Stays in Poland but Doubt He Took A-Secrets

Leopold Infeld has left his post as a professor of applied mathematics at the University of Toronto and re-established himself in his native Poland.

His resignation was tendered, in absentia, in a letter declaring that he had found "excellent conditions for research and scientific work" and for teaching the younger generation in the country which once refused him a professorship . . .

General Władysław Anders, one of Poland's outstanding military leaders during two world wars, was asked for his opinion on the subject. "Impossible!" snapped the general, "I never heard of the man."

During the war, Dr. Infeld worked at Montreal on a small and isolated aspect of the Dominion's atomic projects. It had been unanimously agreed that he should not take part in any of the major work. He was never consulted on problems directly applicable to the work at Chalk River.

Dr. Infeld collaborated with Dr. Albert Einstein in writing *The Evolution of Physics*. The book described, for the intelligent and well-informed layman, the Einstein theory. It has been suggested, since Dr. Infeld announced his intention of remaining in Poland, that he might have acquired information from Einstein which would be of immediate value to the Soviet rulers in the forging of atomic weapons.

This is regarded as highly improbable by persons who understand the immensely complex organization of science needed for the production of the atomic bomb. Dr. Infeld was one of the most capable mathematicians in the world. He was one of the few people who understand in all its details Einstein's unified field theory, successor to and incorporating, the theory of relativity. But Dr. Infeld's knowledge was, in the main, a masterly command of theory, with comparatively insignificant experience of application. . . .

Before Dr. Infeld left Toronto, he had three visits from officials of the Polish Embassy in Ottawa. Dr. Infeld was under the surveillance of the Royal Canadian Mounted Police. He was later kept under the eye of British authorities. He is believed to have made his entry to Poland by way of Paris. . . .

He married Helen Schlauch of New York a short time before coming to Toronto. Mrs. Infeld, also, is a mathematician. But while Dr. Infeld was regarded as an eminent "fellow traveler" his wife was an avowed Communist who had been requested to leave her post with a U.S. university because of her militancy.

But Infeld could be blunt and dogmatic. At a conference on public and international affairs at Lake Couchiching three years ago, he had a sharp brush with Col. W[illiam] W[allace] Goforth, former deputy-general of Canadian defense research.

The thesis Dr. Infeld advanced was: All defense forces became obsolete with the development of the atomic bomb. The only reason defense forces were being maintained was to bolster "the entrenched privilege of the military caste. . . ."

According to Dr. E[dgar] W[illiam] R[ichard] Steacie, vice-president of the National Research Council, Dr. Infeld had no opportunity to partake of Canadian hospitality in the form of data on atomic research.

"We want to point out categorically," said Dr. Steacie, "that Dr. Infeld never had anything to do with our atomic energy project."

Dr. Infeld was employed, at one stage of the Second World War, in complex calculations on ballistics, but no military secrets were involved.

"So far as war research was concerned," Dr. Steacie added, "Dr. Infeld had nothing to do with anything that could be classified as secret."

Although Dr. Steacie did not say so, Dr. Infeld's status in relation to atomic projects would be something lower than "5,000th on the list," according to one observer.

Meantime, the method of Dr. Infeld's resignation suggests a touch of the humour for which he was noted. He had been expected to resume his duties at the University of Toronto on Tuesday.

This article requires a few comments. I can take the news that General Anders never heard of me. But later comes the statement that I worked on the atomic project in Montreal. This, of course, was a lie cut out of whole cloth. The part about Einstein is true, for I know nothing about the atomic bomb; but this contradicts the writer's own statement that I worked on the atomic project in Montreal. That I am one of the best mathematicians in the world I would have to say, modestly, is a great exaggeration.

Other interesting things about myself I learned here for the first time—that I was constantly followed by the Canadian and the British police. All because I wanted to return to my native land for a year. The comments about my wife are false. My disagreement with the Canadian colonel is true, but I could never have used the jargon attributed to me.

Most interesting of all is the conclusion, the statement of Dr. Steacie, Vice-President of the National Research Council in Ottawa, that I never had anything to do with the atomic bomb. Not only that but, in the part of the article I do not quote, there is an official statement by the President of the Council, J[ack] Mackenzie, that I had nothing to do with the atomic bomb. If these statements had only been made a few months earlier I would not have had all that trouble in obtaining my leave to visit Poland, and the whole fuss over my supposedly taking the secret of the atomic bomb would not have arisen. Why didn't these two gentlemen speak up earlier? Perhaps they weren't allowed to or didn't dare, or perhaps they wanted me to leave Canada.

One item from the epilogue of this story. In order to characterize what students thought about my leaving I quote, again only in part, a letter from one of them to the university paper, the *Varsity*. I ought to blush on reading it but I believe it does characterize the atmosphere at the university. I include these extracts with some feeling of pride and embarrassment.

THE LOSS OF INFELD
(*a letter*)

So Leopold Infeld has left Canada! I wish to make a few observations pertinent to this most regrettable occurrence. In the first place I am disappointed—gravely disappointed—in my country for having a part in provoking Professor Infeld to leave our midst, presumably for ever. I am disappointed that some of our nation's leading statesmen have also had a part in it. I am disappointed that the president of this institution had nothing to say in defense of a member of the university staff, a member who has been subjected to the most revolting defamation of character.

One of the Toronto daily newspapers, with a considerably larger circulation than the *Varsity*, but considerably less aggregate editorial mentality, reports that Infeld, an "atomic scientist from the University of Toronto," had at last shown his "true colours" by deserting Canada for the Iron Curtain. It was not specified whether the Iron Curtain mentioned was the one in Europe or the one Conservative Leader George Drew attempted to throw around this country last year to prevent Infeld from leaving on his European lecture tour.... Who among us would consider it a show of this democratic spirit and British justice that a man who never worked on atomics, who never belonged to a Communist organization, whose achievements in the field of applied mathematics have commanded the world's respect for years, should be accused of being a Communist agent who planned to give our atomic secrets to the Reds? When any university in the world would be proud to have Dr. Infeld on its staff, is it surprising that he should leave Canada for his native land—where, we may assume, his talents in his chosen field are more fully appreciated and his views on politics considered of less importance than his transcendent ability in academics?...

Truly, Canada has lost a great man—there was no more intelligent person in this nation. Is it not unfortunate that we were not more appreciative when we were favoured with his presence? Is it not unfortunate that petty politics was allowed to drive him from this country?...

Professor Infeld has demonstrated rather forcibly a fact which seems to have escaped most of us—that the patience of scientists can be tried to the breaking point by the hysterics and witch-hunts of power politics. There is in this incident a lesson to be learned—let us hope that the remaining intelligentsia of this nation will not decide to leave us to the fate which our leaders and a smug populace seem to have planned for us.

[Name on file]

The rest of this story occurred in Warsaw. I received a letter from the Canadian attaché asking me to return my passport. I interpreted this strange request as an order to relinquish citizenship. I returned the passport and resumed my Polish citizenship.

My wife arrived at Gdynia on the *Batory*, two months after me. In fact she came on the Polish national holiday, 22 July

1950. The cold war was at its height. The hot war in Korea had started.

My wife told me the details of the harrassment she had experienced in Toronto. The police dogged her every step, parking in front of the house for hours. They or others made anonymous telephone calls seeking information. Once, when she answered the phone, she heard a voice imitating a child crying, "Come quick, mamma, I hurt myself." This was at the time when our small daughter was due home from school. Another time someone phoned when she was not at home, pretending to be a florist. They asked on which boat and when she was to sail because someone had ordered flowers and they, the florists, had lost the information. Our friend who answered said that he didn't know anything about it and would ask her to phone back. Of course the florists knew nothing about the call.

Eight years later, on 23 December 1958, my daughter and my son— then fifteen and eighteen years old—received notice that their citizenship had been cancelled, although they were Canadian-born. It was interesting that a special Order in Council had been passed for this reason.[3] Why the Canadian government took revenge on my children remains a secret.

The whole affair is sad but it has a gay and even comic ending. The Canadian Ambassador in Poland in the late 1950s and the early 1960s was Hamilton Southam, an exceptionally intelligent man. He and his wife were extremely gracious and charming. He differed from many diplomats in that he liked Poland, became friendly with Polish intellectuals, and sent his children to Polish schools. It was due to his intervention that the national treasures at last returned to their native land. We liked the ambassador very much and had good personal relations with him. He came to me once, not as an ambassador but as a private individual, to tell me that he felt I had been badly used.

After the children's citizenship had been cancelled, I ceased attending official Canadian receptions.

Here I must introduce still another person. My wife's sister,[4] a former professor at New York University, is now a professor at the University of Warsaw. She was once invited to supper at the Canadian Embassy when George Drew was present. Even he came to this Communist country. When talking to my sister-in-law, he asked with great concern after my health and asked her to give me his warm regards.

PLATE 3. The Infeld family in Warsaw 1950.

I arrived in Warsaw with Majewski on a Sunday. He had the key to my apartment at 7 Mazowiecka Street, on the fourth floor. I was glad to see that the building had an elevator, convinced that elevators in Poland behaved like those elsewhere in the world—that they slide easily up and down. I was wrong. Often I had to drag my weak heart up four flights. The apartment itself was a large four-room flat furnished with heavy suites in the nineteenth-century style. I was glad to see what was then rare in Poland, a telephone, and tea and coffee already bought. Dishes, linen—everything had been prepared for us.

The three main windows looked out on the street where buildings were going up opposite. Nearby some had been completed. This view was pleasant, if a bit monotonous. But the view from the other side, in the courtyard, was most depressing. Ruins, heaps of rubble, and just outside our bedroom window bent pipes from a blackened shell swaying in the wind. The view was a constant reminder of what had happened to this city.

My first visit was to Wikta. I had no car, though in two or three days I would have the use of one. I went by taxi. At that time the Warsaw taxis were the oldest models in the world, having several million kilometers on their speedometers. They were pre-war junk of various makes knocked together by the taxi-drivers. Some still had to be cranked. Such taxis have long since vanished from Warsaw streets but then they were the only means of transportation besides the overcrowded streetcars and buses, and the few horse-drawn droshkies.

Wikta received me without warmth. I told her that I had returned to Poland, probably forever. She asked me for the details as though we were talking about an abstract affair, having nothing to do with my or her life. When I argued that my coming for one year probably now meant coming for the rest of my life, that I had no doubt left the West, that I had no way back, she answered that this had been my decision and was not due to her influence. Thus my first visit with Wikta was quite disillusioning.

Later our relations were sometimes better, sometimes worse, but never as warm as in 1949 during my first visit to Poland.

The house in which I lived on Mazowiecka Street was newly built and had no front gate. There was something that served as a gate but it was temporary and made of cheap, unfinished wood, chained on the inside. When I returned home at nine this gate was locked. I knocked, I rang, I beat it, but nobody came. I did not know that one could get in from the other side through the ruins. Thus, on my first day in Poland, I was in a difficult situation—I couldn't return to my own apartment. Fortunately I had my Canadian passport with me and asked for a room in the Hotel Bristol. They gave me their last cubby-hole, where I spent a sleepless night.

More than thirteen years have passed since I returned to Poland. It is time enough to balance the positive and the negative. Let us start with the positive.

When I came to Poland in May of 1950 the university was still in session. Thus I took part in the final seminars of theoretical physics. They were depressing. They were composed of readings from the lectures in an outdated book on field theory. Some student or other lectured, no one asked any questions, and the lecturer himself did not fully understand what he talked about. An atmosphere of boredom prevailed. I tried to break this boredom by asking questions.

The seminars took place every two weeks. Also every two weeks there were seminars in philosophy conducted by an old professor of physics. The small group of listeners could be divided into two parts— young people who liked the professor chiefly because he was known to be religious, and a more radical part that did not like the professor so much. But all of them shared a terrible boredom. Words fell monotonously like driblets of water, and everyone waited for the two hours to pass and bring an end to the philosophical torture.

Such was my first contact with physics in Poland—sad, and revealing its low level. At that time the course in physics lasted only three years. Under such conditions there was no possibility of monographic lectures, and the seminar I visited was not on a scientific level. There was obviously no chance for more lively activity.

I was given a small office where I was alone, then a secretary and a bit of corridor where my two assistants sat. They had come from Krakow and Poznań especially to work with me. In this modest way the Institute of Theoretical Physics had its beginning thirteen years ago; today [1963] it has about fifty scientists.

The first thing the Ministry of Education asked me to do was to organize a summer course. I had had considerable experience in this from Canada.

I was amazed at the generosity of the Ministry. Without much discussion they gave a large sum. Since no one else wanted to undertake it, I arranged for the course to be held in a beautiful mountain resort in the southwest part of Poland—Zakopane. There I met professors and students of physics from the whole country.

While the Ministry showed generosity, the people responsible for organizing the course showed great indifference and lack of a sense of responsibility. The representatives of the Ministry came late to every meeting or didn't come at all. When I went with my family to Zakopane and looked over the building where we were to have the conference, I learned that its director had received some money from the Ministry but had no idea what she was to do with it or for what purpose she had received it. She did not know who was to be the cook or where to get blackboards. And so I had to hire the cook myself, had to look for blackboards in a nearby school and bring them in our car (which I now had) to the building where our course was to be held. I had to prepare everything for the opening. Still, the course was a big success. I discovered the possibilities for physics in Poland, and I met young people who showed great promise.

Soon afterward the academic year began. Suddenly and unexpectedly I found myself very popular. The papers and radio in the country and outside it spread the news that I had left the West and returned to Poland. Because of this popularity I was able to do something towards building up the Institute of Theoretical Physics. As I have said, it was at first a small department with one room where my secretary and I worked. Even to engage a secretary was a difficult task and was accomplished only because of my intervention, since, previously, the assistants had done her work. Secretaries were an unknown institution. (By the way, the same secretary still works with me in the same devoted fashion.)

I realized, of course, that the Institute must grow, and the first requirement was a location. Often, when I was in North America, I said that the president of a university is only interested in acquiring buildings and not in the level of learning. I said that even very modest buildings are sufficient if they house the right people. This is true, but there are some limits beyond which questions of rooms, blackboards, lecture halls become of primary importance. After a long discussion with Professor Pieńkowski, we decided that it would be necessary to enlarge the Institute of Experimental Physics at 69 Hoża Street by adding a new wing, half for experimental and half for theoretical physics. I thought that about 5,000 square feet would be sufficient to take care of the growing needs of the Institute of Theoretical Physics for fifteen years.

We went to the then Vice-Minister Golański who agreed with us after five minutes, promised the money, and proposed that in April of 1951 construction would begin so that in October of the same year it would be finished.

And so we started. We had great difficulties. Judging by our experience, during which we accumulated problems almost impossible to solve, it is incredible to me that so many buildings have been put up so rapidly in Warsaw. Some commission or other decided that we could not build without changing the façade of the whole structure. The plans had to be altered continually because they ran counter to some rule or other. When finally we overcame all these difficulties with many telephone calls and personal visits to ministers and civil servants in high positions, it turned out that the timetable for work was disregarded by everyone and the work was delayed. This job landed me in the hospital for four weeks. I already knew that the October deadline was an illusion, but I declared that I would lecture in the new building on January first. One professor of experimental physics bet me a kilogram of coffee that I would not lecture in the new building by that date. I was very anxious to win the bet (for the coffee, of course!) and so I gave an order that work be concentrated on the lecture hall. At the same time I ordered furniture for this room—a hundred and twenty chairs with broad arms for writing, and a blackboard. The blackboard came on time but the chair factory fell down on the job. Its representative told me that the Ministry of Defence had ordered a hundred and twenty such chairs, which were already made and were only needed in February. If the Ministry would free these chairs, the factory would make an identical hundred and twenty for them on time. I phoned to the Ministry and explained my situation. The answer was that this was a matter for the supply department directed by a certain colonel. I telephoned to him. He was not in but a major was. I told him that the Ministry of Defence could do something for Polish science without harm to itself. The major, after listening to me, said that he had written it all down, must discuss the matter with his higher-ups and that the next day at the latest he would have an answer. An hour later the telephone rang. The chairs were available—the factory had been informed that they should be sent to me. The whole transaction was completed without a single piece of paper, without a shadow of bureaucracy. For two months I tipped my hat whenever I passed the Ministry. Actually I should have sent the major (whose name I have forgotten) half of the coffee I won.

There were other difficulties. For example, according to the rules, the door had to be of pine and if I wanted it to be of oak I had to have the Minister's permission. Buildings could not be stuccoed the same year they were completed—this, too, required special permission from the Minister.

In the spring of 1952 we moved into the new wing where we had fourteen rooms, a fine combined library for the whole Institute, a lecture hall, and a seminar room.

It is interesting to compare the results of my work over twelve years in Canada with those achieved in the same time in Poland. In Canada we had the shabby, small, three-story house for the whole period. When I asked that it at least be painted and cleaned, I always received the same answer, "It's not worth while, the building will be torn down."

In Warsaw we built one wing after my arrival, which I thought would be sufficient for fifteen years. But progress in the socialist country proved to be much more rapid than I had anticipated on my return. After three years the new wing was already too small. We then erected a new building—this time without my personal intervention—which was open for use in 1962.

All this has to do only with the external side of physics. Let us compare the content. In Toronto there were five professors of theoretical physics. One after another they left the university. In 1950 only a colleague and I remained, and, in May of that year, we both left. I trained many Ph.D.s in Toronto, but not one of them was employed by our university for any length of time. Despite my efforts, it was impossible for me to establish a better scientific centre in Toronto.

And in Warsaw? When I arrived I was the youngest of the three professors. Of the two older, one died and the other is now retired. Now, I in turn am the oldest professor. The next after me is twenty-five years younger. Altogether, our Institute now has six professors, two docents (roughly assistant professors), who will soon be appointed to chairs of physics, four other docents, and two devoted secretaries. We deal with various theoretical problems, and our staff members as well as our Ph.D.s are constantly invited to lecture abroad. We maintain a lively contact with both the East and the West.

PLATE 4. Leopold Infeld with a student in Warsaw.

Thus, towards the end of my life, I have accomplished what I always sought—I have developed a good institute of theoretical physics. And this in Poland! It was not even difficult to achieve. For the building of a good institute three things are necessary: to obtain government help in creating jobs and (especially in the beginning) in sending young Ph.D.s abroad for further training; not to restrain young people—on the contrary, to help them to have good conditions for scientific work; to seek young people brighter than one's self and to promote them rapidly.

This is enough. By these means, even if one is already over fifty, when one's scientific inspiration is fading, one can create a good institute.

Now the other side of the medal, the difficulties I had at the time, which were connected mainly—perhaps exclusively—with the Stalin period.

When I came back to Poland, preparations were being made for the Congress of Polish Science. I have no idea in whose brain this idea originated. Unfortunately, I played a certain role in this sad comedy as the Vice-Chairman of the Physics and Mathematics Committee. The preparatory meetings dealt separately with the Physics Committee and the Mathematics Committee. In the former were two dogmatic Marxists, both mediocre scientists, both tactless, who bullied their colleagues. They stated that, while physics hardly existed before the war, only now in a socialist country had it begun to develop, that most important was the study of Marxism, et cetera. I spoke forcefully against their tirades. This loosened the tongues of others who then also spoke against them. Later one of the two dogmatists came to me and accused me of having planned the attack on them in advance and said that I had given the signal by my criticism—I, who was known to be progressive, had served as a cover for the conservatives.

After endless discussions and continual postponements, there was a general congress—a great scientific congress attended by about two thousand professors. I was frightfully bored. One day was supposed to be devoted to general discussion, but ended after one single contribution. At this congress, the Polish Academy of Sciences was announced and soon afterward formed.

The second unpleasantness I experienced was connected with Einstein. When I came to Poland, I was asked to write a book. I

suggested that they translate the one about Einstein already published
in English and was surprised when the publishing house returned the
copy. Only later I learned that, after the translation of *The Evolution
of Physics* had appeared in the Soviet Union, Einstein was regarded
in Poland, too, as an "idealist." Why? Apparently because in our
book we had said that all ideas are free creations of the human mind.
What does this mean? Simply, that our view of the world changes
with time, that fifty years ago our concepts of proton, meson, neutron
did not exist, that our outlook on the objective material world differs
at different times. It depends on the period we are considering, on the
history of physics. In the nineteenth century it was different from in
the twentieth—and today it changes continually. It was entirely
different before the discovery of relativity theory, different before the
existence of quantum theory, and different again after these theories
were formulated.

The objection that *The Evolution of Physics* was "idealistic" seems
to me unjustified. Both Einstein and I regarded ourselves as material-
ists, though neither of us had then studied the theory of dialectical
materialism. Looking at it today, I would say that the philosophical
parts contain some formulations that could be interpreted as "idealistic." But this "idealism" of Einstein is far more interesting than the
dialectical materialism of certain sectarians who attacked the book.
Thus, for example, I was told that a certain Mr. Z said at a public
meeting, "Einstein is an idealist and Infeld is doing his work in
Poland." When I heard this I answered, "I prefer to be criticized in
the company of Einstein than praised in the company of Mr. Z."

This was during the period of "errors and distortions."

Some of the objections were made by philosophers who had no
idea of physics and opposed relativity theory as an "idealistic" theory.
One of these objections was that we were supposed to have come out
against the theory of Copernicus. I went into this matter at length in
my article "From Copernicus to Einstein,"[5] from which I would
like to quote:

> I should like to remove at least one misunderstanding that exists in the
> interpretation of relativity theory. It is sometimes said that relativity
> theory claims there is no difference between the theories of Copernicus
> and Ptolemy, that from the point of view of theory it is immaterial

which is used. Such comments result either from a real or a wilful misunderstanding. The fault sometimes lies with popularizers who are not sufficiently exact, but in no case would anyone who had really studied relativity theory reach such a conclusion. If it is a question of the mathematical structure of relativity theory, the invariance does reveal, indeed, that the idea of a coordinate system is not necessary and that there is no difference (I repeat: from the point of view of the mathematical theory) between Ptolemy's and Copernicus's systems. But physical meaning is quite a different matter.

The mathematical representation of a concrete part of reality, like the motion of a planet, the motion of two bodies, the curvature of light rays, is completely objective and is referred either to a coordinate system connected with the sun, or with the centre of mass—that is, to a Copernican coordinate system. Relativity theory, as a means of understanding nature, employs the Copernican coordinate system to the same extent as Newtonian theory. It is superior to the Newtonian theory in that it does not require an inertial coordinate system. Furthermore, its results are more in agreement with observation than are those of Newtonian theory. In the theory of measurements which we must add to every theory, we assume that the measurements are made by an observer far from the sun and that, for him, the gravitational field is very weak. The Earth and the observer intervene in physics only through the theory of measurements. Such a theory is required to draw conclusions, from the results of the measurements, regarding nature and the rules governing the objective world. It seems to me certain that relativity theory is a great step forward in our knowledge, that its physical meaning, consistent with experiment, must be in complete agreement with a basic materialistic understanding. That certain formulations of this theory appear to be idealistic is connected with the fact that the theory is very difficult and requires many years of thought and a knowledge of the appropriate mathematical methods. Since it was formulated in the West, it can easily be interpreted as idealistic by philosophers. Even with the best of intentions, philosophers may fail to understand relativity theory. People often have the desire to condemn things that they do not understand, and the attacks on relativity theory, one of the greatest creations of the human mind, find their source precisely here.

By arguing with the philosophers who oppose relativity theory I am probably trying to force doors that are already open, since much has changed recently in this field both in the Soviet Union and in Poland.

The fight against sectarians is now especially sharp, and determinism is understood to be the enemy of science.

The last three pages of our book were attacked most vociferously. In the last chapter, entitled "Physics and Reality," we wrote that science is composed of ideas and concepts that are the free creations of the human mind.

For some critics this smelled of pure Berkeleyism. We explained what we understood by this sentence in the chapter "The Riddle of Motion," as follows:

> Physical concepts are free creations of the human mind, and are not, however it may seem, uniquely determined by the external world. In our endeavour to understand reality we are somewhat like a man trying to understand the mechanism of a closed watch. He sees the face and the moving hands, even hears its ticking, but he has no way of opening the case. If he is ingenious he may form some picture of a mechanism which would be responsible for all the things he observes, but he can never be quite sure his picture is the only one which could explain his observations. He will never be able to compare his picture with the real mechanism and he cannot even imagine the possibility or the meaning of such a comparison. But he certainly believes that, as his knowledge increases, his picture of reality will become simpler and simpler and will explain a wider and wider range of his sensuous impressions. He may also believe in the existence of the ideal limit of knowledge and that it is approached by the human mind. He may call this ideal limit the objective truth.[6]

I think it is clear that between the fragments of reality we describe and the concepts by means of which we describe them, there does not exist a unique correspondence. This is obvious if we consider the difference between everyday and scientific language. For example, imagine the descriptions of a rock as written by an ordinary observer, a minerologist, a chemist, a physicist, an atomic or nuclear physicist. Besides this difference between the everyday and scientific language, there is also the difference within scientific language as science advances. The concepts we use to describe our real world undergo changes. For example, consider the theories of light given by Huygens, by Newton, and by Einstein's photons. As we come to know reality better and better, I believe that we approach a complete correspondence between our description and the material world, that we approach objective truth. If there were thinking beings on Mars, they would have—within limits—the same physics as we do.

No doubt what I write here and what we wrote in our book is not, and was not, expressed in the terminology of dialectical materialism, but the declaration that the authors are pure idealists can result only from ignorance or malice or a mixture of these two human failings which often appear together.

In the time of "errors and distortions," many philosophers of various levels assailed Einstein, [Linus] Pauling, [Werner] Heisenberg, Dirac, [Lev Davidovich] Landau, [Abram Fedorovich] Joffe—the dean of Soviet physicists—and also me. Today their articles are of no interest to anyone and no physicist even reads them. But it is worth while to consider more deeply the influence of philosophers on physics.

What do we understand by philosophy and whom do we call a philosopher? There are at least three different answers to these questions.

By a philosopher of physics (or of any other subject), I understand a physicist whose chief interest lies with the methods and foundations of physics. In this meaning Einstein said of himself: "I am more a philosopher than a physicist." In this way [Arnold] Sommerfeld called Einstein the greatest modern philosopher.[7] In this sense everyone who applies Marxist methods to the social sciences, to history, to economics, and is at the same time a specialist in the field, acts as a philosopher.

But the word philosopher is also used in quite a different sense. Throughout antiquity and the dark ages, before the greatest development of science—that is, before the sixteenth century—people tried to understand the world in which they lived. They thought they could understand it, not through experiment based on mathematical analysis, but by pure speculation and the useless play of words. These dramatic attempts can be of interest only to the history of science. In this way arose the history of philosophy and the historians of philosophy who are also called philosophers. They deal with problems that have no sense from the point of view of science. Of what interest is it for me in the twentieth century that some Greek or other said that the world is composed of four elements? I do understand, however, that there are people who are fascinated by this, and, indeed, I think there are too many of them.

But there is yet a third type of philosopher who is truly harmful. This is the one who imagines that still, today, one can create the truth about our world out of thin air by means of pure speculation. Such men are not physicists, they are not mathematicians, but they would like to control physics and mathematics. Fortunately for science, this type of philosopher is dying out today.

Another objection to our book was connected with the following argument. Einstein allegedly said that, from the point of view of relativity theory, it was immaterial whether the earth turned around the sun or the sun around the earth. This was taken to mean that Copernicus was not right, that there is no difference between the theories of Ptolemy and Copernicus, and thus Einstein had come out against Copernicus.

In Poland this objection was particularly sharp because there had long been a Copernican cult here. He was not only the greatest scientist of all time, but also a great man. Glorification, idolatry—these are old Polish weaknesses. Of course these arguments were without foundation, for the theory of Copernicus is still valid, though only when applied to a limited range of facts. Old theories are correct if we confine ourselves to the facts they explain. Copernicus was right—our earth turning around the sun explains many facts much better than does the sun turning around the earth. But the path of the earth that better fits the facts of planetary motion was found only after the great discovery of Kepler, who placed the Copernican theory in the proper light.

Einstein's theory does not change Copernicus's conception of the earth moving around the sun; rather, the situation is formulated differently. Einstein's theory was necessary because new facts were discovered that did not fit the theories of Copernicus, Kepler, and Newton; these were explained by Einstein. His theory reformulated Copernicus's view of the earth's motion in the following way: we must choose a coordinate system connected with the sun that is Euclidian at infinity. Such is the formulation of Copernicus's theory in Einstein's language. This reformulation came only after four hundred years, when all the old theories had only historical significance. And so it is simply a mistake to say that Copernicus's theory does not agree with Einstein's.

By this example we can also see how wrong was the first objection, stating that our concepts are not the free creations of the human mind.

In Einstein's theory we choose the coordinate system connected with the sun and, in this way, formulate Copernicus's view in a way quite different from the one he used.

The lack of reason lodged in these objections was connected with the isolation of science during Stalinist times. There was no intellectual interchange between East and West, so essential for the rapid and proper development of science, an international enterprise. I never questioned the level of science in the Soviet Union, but I believe that the result of isolation for certain scientists of that country was a loss of proportion in evaluating some phenomena—for example, in attributing to Soviet scientists many discoveries known to the world as the achievements of others.

During those years an article was published in the Soviet Union about relativity theory, claiming that Einstein had plagiarized, copying the theory from [Nikolai Ivanovich] Lobachevsky. In other words, what was correct in Einstein's theory had already been discovered by Lobachevsky. (Unfortunately this silly revelation was translated into Polish and published in a pamphlet on relativity theory.)

Of course it is quite possible that someone in Russia worked on the steam engine simultaneously with—or even earlier than—[George] Stephenson. But what matters is that the West was then prepared for the discovery, and that civilization had reached a level where the use of the steam engine was necessary.

Up to 1953 I had complete freedom in lecturing on relativity theory and in talking about it. But, in 1953, my situation began to be somewhat complicated. Perhaps because I have a deeply rooted custom of making independent judgments, the mere fact that a theory is formulated in the Soviet Union is not sufficient to convince me of its truth. Neither [Olga Borisnova] Lepishynaska nor [Trofim Denisovich] Lysenko were authorities for me.

Some role in changing my position with officialdom was played by a discussion I had with Professor [Vladimir Alexandrovich] Fock. He is an outstanding Soviet theoretical physicist, on a very high level, who came out for a change in Einstein's theory while retaining its mathematical skeleton, and he believed that he had much improved the theory. As it developed later, all the well-known Soviet physicists were against this effort. But in Poland it was assumed that Fock, as a Soviet scientist, must be right.

PLATE 5. Leopold Infeld at home, about 1954.

I met Professor Fock in 1952. At the time there was almost no contact between Polish and Soviet science. It was then possible to go to the West. Privileged persons did so quite often and I was one of them. I went to England, Italy, Norway, Sweden, Switzerland, but I did not then go to the Soviet Union despite the fact that I let it be understood that I would like to see that country and travel east. However, until then I had neither seen nor met a single Soviet scientist.

After 1950 and the success in Zakopane, a conference of Polish physicists was held every summer. Organized by me, these became known as "Infeldiads." In 1952 one of them was held in Spała, a small resort town two hours from Warsaw, used as a summer home by the pre-war president Ignacy Mościcki. The Ministry of Science and Higher Education invited Soviet scientists, not giving any names— merely asking for their cooperation. The Soviet Union sent a delegation of three physicists of whom the most important was Professor Fock. In this way I met him together with two other Soviet physicists.

Of course, this conference in 1952 was something of an occasion, and, for the first time, a vice-minister and delegates of the Central Committee of the Polish United Workers Party attended. Naturally, Polish Marxist philosophers were also invited.

As the chairman of the organizing committee I opened the conference and greeted the Soviet guests. I spoke objectively about the truly great scientific contribution of Professor Fock. In reply, he made a short, pleasant statement which ended: "Long live [Bolesław] Bierut, First Citizen of the Polish state." To this there was no way out but to thank him and say for the first time in my life: "Long live Stalin, First Citizen of the Soviet Union." Afterward a certain important official who had been present objected that I should have said: "Long live Stalin, the leader of progressive mankind."

Who is this Fock? Black hair, fairly fat, around sixty, pleasant, somewhat like Einstein externally. He had an attractive way about him, laughed gaily, was deaf, and wore a hearing aid which—so the spiteful said—he turned off when the argument of his opponent did not please him. He was dogmatic and very much believed in his own convictions. I may say that, during this time, I became friendly with Fock. Our relations were better than correct. I argued with him, tried to convince him that he was wrong, but of course without result. Officially I could only react mildly to his objections to Einstein's

77

equations of motion. I must add that Fock's solution of the problem of motion was made without a knowledge of the basic work done by Einstein, Hoffmann and me.[8] His solution came a year later than ours and was only for Newtonian motion, which was incomparably easier than the solution that we gave and that Fock and his student obtained eight years later.[9]

As I remarked, this was in 1952. And it was in 1953 that the unpleasant atmosphere gathered around me. This is how it was. On the proposal of President Bierut, the Polish Academy of Sciences was created in April of 1952. Before this, Bierut had invited me to come to Belvedere Palace, his official residence. For the first time, if I do not count previous several-minute meetings at receptions, I met and talked for more than an hour with the President of the country. He impressed me favourably as someone versed in scientific problems and having the proper respect for them. He told me that when he had been in prison he had read my book *Nowe drogi nauki* [*New Pathways of Science*], and then he complimented me on it.[10]

When the Academy was established, those who became its members for the most part deserved the distinction, although, in addition, there were some whose service to science was unknown and others—though very few—who were chosen for quite extraneous reasons.

The President asked me who, in my opinion, ought to be members of the Academy from physics and mathematics. Then he told me that its president would be Professor Jan Dembowski, and the secretary-general would be Professor Stanisław Mazur. Before the war Dembowski was a professor in Vilna. I knew that he was a progressive and that he had written a good popular book on biology. I was not familiar with his scientific work. He made a poor impression when I met him.

At the first meeting of the presidium of the Academy, Dembowski delivered a welcoming speech in which he stated that Polish science ought to follow in the footsteps of Soviet science. He mentioned Lysenko and Lepishynska without saying a word about the great Polish physicist [Marian] Smoluchowski or Madame Sklodowska-Curie. Dembowski was the President of the Academy and later Marshal of the Seym [Parliament]. Thus, he held two important posts in Poland—one scientific and one political.

Professor Mazur is a well-known mathematician, and I have always regarded him as having a strong and righteous character.

Poland

In 1953 it was suggested that the Academy arrange a great ceremony to honour the memory of Copernicus. It was to be in 1953 because the real 400th anniversary of the appearance of *De revolutionibus* and his death came during the war in 1943 when there could be no ceremony. Various scientists were invited for the delayed celebration, including Professor Fock.

I had been working for twenty years on the two-body problem, a Copernican problem. I had worked on it with Einstein for ten years. Yet, although I was not invited to give a lecture at this ceremony, a young man from Wrocław was. I considered this an affront. Another who did not take part in this occasion was Professor [Tadeusz] Banachiewicz, the greatest Polish astronomer since Copernicus.

Another incident: Professor Mazur told me that the Soviet Union wished to present Poland with some documents connected with Copernicus. He asked me if I would like to be on the delegation to receive them. As I have said, inasmuch as I had never been to the Soviet Union, I gladly agreed. But I was not sent.

On weekends I often went to Nieborów, the former palace of the Radziwiłłs, now a museum where there were a number of guest rooms for artists, writers, and scientists. This was one of the few stately homes near Warsaw that the Nazis did not have time to destroy. It was further saved from theft and vandalism by the present museum director, who followed the retreating Germans immediately and protected the building. It was, therefore, just as it had been before the war except for the natural accumulation of dirt and wear. (Now, in 1963, it has been renovated, even to the painted gold emblem on the coat-of-arms outside.)

It was the custom for all the guests to gather at mealtimes around one large table in the beautiful Nieborów dining room. We looked upon the large paintings of the Canaletto school set in the walls, the graceful white carved ceiling, the well-proportioned lines of the room and the old Radziwiłł silver still gleaming dully in the built-in cabinets at one end of the room. The original furniture was still there, and old hangings at the windows were threadbare remains of earlier grandeur.

On one occasion, the person sitting opposite me at dinner was Zygmunt Modzelewski, a very influential Party member. He was a retired Minister of Foreign Affairs, a very intelligent man in poor health, and was also a member of the Academy. During the general conversation he said to me that Einstein was an "idealist" and was recognized only in the West. Angry, I answered in front of everyone: "You talk about things of which you understand nothing!"

He blushed, but answered not a word. I should mention that, despite this incident, relations between us remained good, even improved. Modzelewski never tried to take revenge on me for my sharp rejoinder.

Fock's article, translated from the Russian, appeared in *Mysl Filosoficzna* [*Philosophical Thought*].[11] It contained his own interpretation of relativity theory. From this work it would appear that he had invented the principles of motion in relativity theory and that we had committed plagiarism in publishing them a year later. Actually not a year, but nine years earlier we were supposed to have committed a double plagiarism! This was a bit too much. I wrote a short letter to the editor of *Philosophical Thought*, putting the matter straight. I heard later that the discussion in the editorial board lasted all night as to whether to include the letter, but in the end common sense prevailed and it was published. Then I wrote an article in defence of Einstein and it, too, after some discussion, was printed in the same periodical.[12]

At this time Stalin died. At first we felt no change. They say that in the Soviet Union it was felt at once. They stopped saying that Stalin was a genius, now he became merely great. Only later came the news of the Beria affair, of Malenkov's removal, and, finally, of the Twentieth Congress and the Polish October changes.

My unfortunate experiences were much fewer than my successes. For it was during this time that I organized a scientific institute. There was never a lack of money in the Ministry for new positions. The Ministry fulfilled all requests related to the institute, which was branching out in many directions other than relativity theory, since I believed that other fields were more necessary for the country—for example the theory of solid-state physics and nuclear theory.

I cannot complain of my fate. But an interesting question does remain: what happened to other professors on whom the pressure was greater? I must say that, as far as I know, no one touched even a hair of their heads during my time in Poland. Yet the political pressure was quite strong and led a number of people to indulge in "self-criticism"—they confessed "I didn't understand properly but now I see the light." For some, this self-criticism opened the way to a career,

PLATE 6. Leopold Infeld at the weekly seminar of the Institute of Theoretical Physics, Warsaw.

for others it did not suffice. Only once was I present during such an experience. Ever since I have a bad feeling when I remember that meeting.

In Krakow, in 1950, there was a physics conference to which I did not wish to go. However, colleagues insisted that I ought to be there. And so I went to my native city for two days. I gave a report on my work on the equations of motion in Einstein's new unitary theory. I observed the two-hour ideological meeting at which one physicist, a good physicist who was under the influence of ideological bullying exerted by the same two physicists I mentioned in connection with the Congress of Science, committed a self-criticism that was warmly received. From that time on he had peace.

This was the most general but not the only form of pressure. There was another type—exerted by students belonging to the youth organization. Their leaders had an important voice in accepting students to the university, granting them prizes and scholarships, granting awards to professors and estimating their work. I experienced only one attempt at such interference. There was a young student in the Experimental Physics Institute secretly called "the little Stalin." At the time he had great influence. Once he came to me to protest against the examinations in my institute, quite without reason. Our very brief conversation ended with this—that I asked him to close the door behind him.

Once, before I went abroad, a young woman student applied for a graduate fellowship. She was very capable, good material for a future scientist, and so I approved her application. When I returned from abroad I learned that she had been refused. I telephoned to the Ministry and asked why. I was told that "little Stalin" had a negative opinion of her because she too often attended church. I answered that if she were not granted the fellowship in twenty-four hours, I would resign from my position. And the next day she received notice of her acceptance. I must admit that this was probably my only quarrel with the Ministry, and even in this case the Minister immediately gave in.

Any theory which was not accepted by Soviet scientists but only by Western scientists was looked upon as "idealist." [13] This was the case with Wiener's cybernetics. This was the case with Einstein and Pauling. I don't know the latter's theory but I have enough confidence in Pauling as a scientist and a man to believe that one cannot destroy his theory with the word "idealist." But in Poland before my return there had been a conference of chemists at which a physicist gave a lecture on Pauling's theory, and all the chemists present voted that it was "idealist" rather than scientific. This reaction to Pauling was especially strange since he was a progressive man, looked upon with disfavour by conservative Americans but much admired by liberals—a man who has devoted his life to the preservation of peace.

Professor Joffe was the dean of the Soviet experimental physicists. He had trained a whole generation. He had done much for the Soviet Union. Nevertheless, it was held against him that his understanding of the equation $E = mc^2$, which was already being shouted from the housetops all over the world, was not in agreement with Stalinist dialectics.

The great Landau, coauthor with Lifschitz of the most modern textbook on field theory, one of the greatest theoretical physicists in the world, did not escape attack. His book on mechanics was sharply criticized and he himself was under pressure.[14]

It was still worse with philosophers than with physicists. The only accepted direction for philosophy was Marxism. And everyone had to study Marxist philosophy—not only students but also the administrative staff. Only the older professors were excused from Marxist courses. Suddenly many people were designated experts in this field, and most of their lectures were on a very low level. I consider myself a Marxist, but I do not believe that Marxism can be contained in a dogmatic formula. I believe that Marxism, which explains many economic problems and historical events, has much meaning for mankind as a method. But in these Marxist courses the main interpretation was Stalinist. He was the saint—Stalin was supposed to be the greatest linguist, the greatest economist. He was supposed to have discovered a brilliant economic law—I don't know in what it consists, but the Polish economists pronounced it from their pulpits.

The older, pre-war professors of philosophy were not allowed to lecture. Fortunately they did not die of hunger but were paid full salaries. Indeed, they then had plenty of free time. The philosophers, and especially the sociologists, recalled this time nostalgically because they were then able to do research to their hearts' content.

Although when I now look back on those days they appear very glum, at the time I was not aware of it. Perhaps I was too busy building my institute, perhaps I was too much occupied with my frequent trips to the West. Most important, I did not personally feel any lack of political freedom; I was only distressed by a lack of scientific freedom. But the political pressure became more and more intense. True, we had no such affairs as that of Slánský in Czechoslovakia[15] but there was the affair of Gomułka, who had been imprisoned before my return to Poland.[16]

My eyes were opened to what was happening only when, in the last months of Stalin's life, it was reported that over a dozen Jewish doctors had been jailed in the Soviet Union. They were supposed to have been bribed by pounds sterling and English razor blades to kill Stalin and other Soviet officials. It was a shocking accusation. Then, for the first and only time in my life, I regretted that I had returned to Poland. But soon the Stalin era ended—Stalin died. I was afraid that it might be still worse, but the atmosphere slowly began to improve and, since then, I have never regretted my decision to return.

The year 1953. What an analogy with the year a hundred and sixty years before—the year 1793 in France—the period of the greatest horror ending with the murder of Robespierre! I had studied that period carefully when I was writing *Whom the Gods Love*, but I never imagined that it would have any association with my native land. At first I had no idea what was going on. Things went well for me. I had my institute and closed my eyes to the rest, about which some people told me. I closed my eyes to the fact that many innocent people were in jail. I believed that most of those accused had undoubtedly done something wrong. Of course, mistakes might be made, but these were few. Yet during the next three years I slowly came to know that these mistakes were not accidental, but rather the rule. I met people who had been released from prison. They were sent to hospitals for cures, they were paid damages, given apartments, publicly exonerated. There were many such. Alas, not all lived long enough to experience this pleasant change.

Up to the time of Stalin's death, I thought that the terror was the work not of Stalin but of people around him. When the paper *Izvestia* chose me from among thirty million Poles (I don't know why) to write a few words about Stalin's death, I wrote a short article about which I wonder, today, whether I should blush or laugh.

I remember that in the Seym there was a meeting in honour of Stalin's memory at which a well-known economist delivered a speech.

A physicist took the floor, naturally agreeing with the party line. During Stalin's time all "discussions" were agreed upon in advance, read from paper, almost never spontaneous or unprepared. And so it was with one of the best physicists in Poland—a young man who attacked Einstein for being an "idealist." He praised Soviet science to the skies. It would have been a terrible sin on my part not to attend the meeting. This was, I think, the last time I heard Einstein publicly called an "idealist."

I believe it was in 1954 that the improvement started for me, as far as science was concerned. It began when the editor of *Philosophical Thought* came to see me, and told me that my article defending the theory of relativity was to be published in the most important Soviet philosophical journal. The attacks on Einstein ceased. Once again his name was raised to that of the greatest scientist of all time. In Poland I also felt the echo of this triumph. In 1954 I was given the Standard of Labour, First Class.

The curtains that enclosed Poland on East and West lifted suddenly and dramatically, and the way was open to a free flow of people and ideas in both directions.

The year 1955 was an eventful one for me. It began sadly. I was in Nieborów when the news came over the radio that Einstein had died. Those around me kept it from me so that only after I returned to Warsaw did I learn about it. Polish and foreign publications asked me for articles about Einstein, but I was still too upset to comply. I wrote only one page which appeared in several Polish papers and *L'Humanité*. Later the Polish author, now president of the Polish Writers' Union, Jarosław Iwaszkiewicz, told me that the monthly *Twórczość [Creativity]* wanted a longer essay about Einstein. I liked the idea and prepared an article with the title "My Memories of Einstein." [17] Slightly enlarged and changed, it now forms a part of this book. In it, I tried to express the respect and admiration I have always had, and will always have, for Einstein.

Unexpectedly, I received an invitation to the Soviet Union—to attend a conference on field theory in Moscow. The Soviet Academy of Sciences invited one person from each country of the Socialist bloc. Thus, at last, I was to have the chance to satisfy my curiosity. It was indeed an interesting experience. At the border station I waited six hours while the train was changed to broad-gauge. The Brest station was full of life, of people—officers and women in fantastic, elaborately designed hats.

In Moscow one is impressed by the broad streets, the height of some of its buildings, especially the university skyscraper. At the National Hotel where I stayed there was still a large portrait of Stalin in the lobby downstairs. Although modest, the hotel was quite good.

I went to the Lenin-Stalin mausoleum outside of which long queues wait patiently for hours every day. We foreigners, however, were taken in directly. Stalin's grim face overshadowed the intelligent face of Lenin. Stalin lay dressed in the uniform of a generalissimo. He looked alive but asleep. This was a sight that will not be seen by future generations.[18]

I also visited the Kremlin museum—rich with silver, gold, rare china, and jewels. I saw the crown of Ivan the Terrible, Peter's boots, and the old Russian official decorations. I also saw the Greek Orthodox churches in the Kremlin with their onion domes, full of gold and icons. It all seemed very foreign to me, as if belonging to another, though powerful world. The tremendous activity in the streets, the number of uniforms, the crowds of people in the shops, all this astonished me. The whole city pulsed with life and force.

It was interesting to meet Professor [Igor] Tamm, a most charming man. He was extremely lively and, although older than me, was a well-known mountain climber. When I spoke to him of Fock, he told me that all the Soviet physicists were opposed to Fock's under-standing of relativity theory, and he proposed that we have an evening of open discussion on Fock's objections to the theory of relativity. I gladly agreed.[19]

I met Lev Landau, the greatest Soviet physicist and one of the greatest in the world. He was younger than I—at the time under fifty. Somewhat similar to Dirac, he was slim, with a crop of hair that fell forward over his eyes, with a sharp tongue for his colleagues and all physicists. Despite this, he had the charm of a young boy who has jumped into physics and is thrilled by it. He only talked well about two people—Fermi and Einstein. About other physicists he generally spoke ironically and humorously.

While I spoke English with Tamm and Landau, I could speak Polish with [Nikolai Nikolaevich] Bogoliubov. Later I learned that

Bogoliubov had been in love with a Polish actress when he was young and that was why he had learned the language. He was very pleasant, an excellent theoretical physicist who had given up mathematics for physics.

We were then subjected to the torture of Russian hospitality, about which I had heard in Poland. To give an idea, I shall describe the first day of the conference. In the morning, breakfast was prepared in a small room of the National Hotel. There were six delegates—five from Socialist countries and one from the West. At about ten in the morning we were taken to a table set for breakfast. It was covered with a variety of good things: salted fish, cold cuts, sour milk, and coffee (which is mostly drunk in Moscow with lemon), cakes and eggs, so that we went with full stomachs to the Academy.

There, for the first time, I met Tamm, Landau, and Bogoliubov. Bogoliubov greeted us, then there was conversation over tea and cakes, which we again had to consume out of politeness. After this pleasant talk we went to lunch. It was heavy. The first course consisted of caviar, fish, and cold cuts. Then there was a rich soup—Russian borscht, then meat and cakes for dessert. Lunch ended between four and five o'clock and soon after we went to the Lebedev Institute. We passed along the wide streets with their huge buildings, interspersed with small wooden houses. The contrast between the old and new Moscow existing side by side, was a striking one. The institute was not of modern architecture but rather of the nineteenth century. The meetings were held in the large hall seating several hundred people. The reports were read from the rostrum on which there were two blackboards.

After Professor Tamm greeted us, Landau gave a report. A summary of the text in English was given to us, and, next to each foreigner, sat a physicist who could translate what was being said on the rostrum from Russian into English. Next to me sat Lifschitz who had long worked with Landau. With him it was a pleasure to gossip about the complicated relations among Soviet physicists.

Landau's lecture was on quantum field theory. It was deep, offering a critical appraisal of field theory—the same that later appeared in the volume to celebrate Bohr's seventieth year.[20]

Before the official opening there had been a small reception in the Lebedev Institute—again with tea and cakes immediately after a huge lunch, in a room decorated with large colour photographs of the members of the Political Bureau. That evening we all went to the opera in the Bolshoi Theater. The richness of presentation was striking. There were five hundred people on the stage, there were horses and riders, realistic decorations—a style then flourishing in the Soviet Union. I am no expert on singing and have no special fondness for opera, but I was impressed by the careful production and the splendid acting. In the crowd and the chorus, each had his own role to play. There was a great difference between the opera I saw in Milan and the one presented here. In Milan there was no evident direction, the crowd behaved as it liked, each doing as he chose, as in an amateur performance. In Milan the one thing that mattered was that the voices were rich and beautiful. But here everything was very exact, thought out to the last detail.

Most interesting for me was the discussion between Fock and the Soviet physicists, in which I also took part. One day this discussion replaced the afternoon session. First Fock spoke and formulated his objections to Einstein's theory by defining his own conception of harmonic coordinate systems. Then I spoke in favour of Einstein's theory and was followed by Landau, Tamm, and [Vitali Lazarevich] Ginzburg—all well-known physicists who preferred Einstein's theory to Fock's. They said that his additional equations for defining the coordinate system are unnecessary and provide nothing of value. Fock still stuck to his interpretation of the theory, as he does today, but I learned during my visit to Moscow that he was fairly isolated at the time.

At the farewell banquet I met Professor [Peter] Kapitza, a very intelligent man and the least conventional of the Soviet physicists. He looked just the same as he had when I had met him twenty years before in England. His hair was somewhat greyer, but his face was just about the same, just as intelligent. We talked of various things—of England, of East-West relations, of the puzzles he liked to pose. One was as follows: A dog has a metal frying pan attached to his tail. Wherever the dog runs the frying pan scrapes on the pavement. The question is: with what speed must the dog run so that he can't hear the sound of the scraping? Landau and I tried to work it out. Finally Kapitza took pity on us and gave the obvious answer. (The answer is contained in line 15 of page 105.)

After the conference we went on an excursion to Leningrad. There it was cold in the hotel and cold on the street. I froze the whole time and the cold spoiled Leningrad for me, but I did not fail to appreciate the wide squares, colourful buildings, streets, statues, and especially the thrilling Hermitage Museum. There I saw two paintings by Leonardo da Vinci, a Bruegel, and twenty-six Rembrandts. In addition, I wanted to see the French nineteenth-century collection. I was taken to a section of the builiding far from the main halls, high up. With someone else who wanted to see the French paintings, I climbed many stairs up to the attic. I saw rooms filled with Renoirs, Gaugins, Cezannes, gems of French painting. Just the two of us looked at it all, while the other parts of the building were crowded with spectators.

It was also in Leningrad that I first saw the inside of a Soviet scientist's apartment. Fock, who was cordial to me in spite of our differences concerning the theory of relativity, invited me to his home. The door was opened by a woman who was not present during the abundant high tea. To this day I do not know whether she was his wife or his housekeeper. Fock's apartment was full of antiques and crowded with papers and books.

In July of 1955 there was to be a meeting of relativists in Berne, Switzerland, to commemorate the fiftieth anniversary of relativity theory. I went with my wife and for the first time met nearly all the world's relativists. It was the first time I met Pauli, one of the greatest scientists of our century, whose path I had never crossed. We had corresponded, but I had never seen that ugly, highly intelligent face, that amusing behaviour, that bobbing of his whole torso during others' lectures, his constant nodding yes or no, his loud uncontrolled behaviour. Pauli was an extraordinarily intelligent man. His intelligence, his interest and understanding of modern physics were truly astonishing. His criticism of others was unsuppressed, spiteful but never bitter, and seldom enthusiastic. He was known for his sharp answers and his irony, although his remarks were always delivered with a sense of humour. I would say that Pauli was the conscience of contemporary physics. He would come out against a theory apparently without reason, but later it always turned out that there had been a deep basis for his position. If, sometimes, the theory he attacked was proved right by experiment (for example in the case of parity), he quickly changed his position and became enthusiastic. He was fat, small, with reddened eyes. I think he must have already been ill although it did not show. Unfortunately, he died two years later.

There were many stories told among physicists about Pauli, legends growing with time. Some were true, others half true, and still others probably untrue. Even though they often had to do with his extreme arrogance, I know no other physicist who had more true friends and admirers. I shall give one story that was told to me by one of his students.

Physicists and mathematicians often use the term "trivial" to denote something that is true but for which the proof is simple and apparent. Pauli's statement that "everything seems trivial when we understand it" was repeated throughout the world of physicists. Once, during his seminar, Pauli made a statement the proof of which he regarded as trivial. One of the students said that to him it did not seem trivial, and he didn't see how to prove it. It turned out that Pauli also did not see and he began to write with chalk on the blackboard, bobbing up and down the while. But it did not come out. Whereupon he left the room and went into his office. He stayed away ten minutes. Then Pauli returned to the room and announced: "The proof *is* trivial." And he went on to other things.[21]

In Berne I also met Dr. [Otto] Nathan, whom Einstein had named as executor of his will. We had hoped that Einstein would be at the meeting in Berne, but he had died a few months before. Nathan told me that Einstein had stated in his will that his funeral was to be secret, that no one was to know where he was buried. Indeed, Nathan did not betray to anyone what was done with his ashes. Apparently the funeral took place early in the morning, at about five o'clock, and was attended by Nathan, Einstein's closest family, and his secretary. In the hospital Einstein was working to the last moment. When Nathan bade him farewell, in the morning, Einstein asked for the paper on which he, himself, was still working. In the afternoon, when Nathan returned to the hospital, he learned that Einstein had died.

Berne is a clean, beautiful city, full of shops selling watches. It lies on the River Aar amid hills and mountains. It has a famous clock which is the scene of a strange event every hour. Figures beat hammers, elves appear, and goats jump. Around this clock there is always a crowd waiting for the hour to strike.

Poland

After the conference in Berne my wife and I went to Val-Mont to await the next conference three weeks later—the first Atoms for Peace Conference in Geneva. It was a large conference organized by the United Nations and was attended by both East and West. Then, for the first time, I felt that there was peace on earth. Such was the outbreak of good will and friendly relations between the representatives of the Soviet Union and the West that I felt it marked the beginning of lasting scientific cooperation. Later came the meeting of the Big Four, and I along with many others believed that peace was assured for the future, that the end of international tension was near.

In 1955 I also accepted an invitation to visit China. The invitation had come some time before from the Chinese Academy, but my ill health had not allowed me to accept it. At that time the doctors believed that I should avoid flying (especially by unpressurized planes) in favour of trains. My wife went along to look after me. First we went to Moscow where I acted as Helen's guide. Once again I saw the mausoleum, the Kremlin, the Eastern churches. Then, by a most comfortable train, we went on to Peking. The trip took about ten days in all.

Only by travelling across it does one get an impression of the Soviet Union's grandeur. The borderline between Europe and Asia is supposed to be the Ural Mountains. I had imagined that the Urals would be massive like the Rocky Mountains in Canada or the Alps or the Tatras. Nothing of the sort. One is not aware of a transition, one sees no mountains between Europe and Asia. The existence of the Urals is a myth. Unfortunately, the timetable is such that the train passes the most beautiful spot, Lake Baikal, at night. We saw large cities and rivers only from the windows of the train. The social life of the train was concentrated at the stations. At the longer stops (over ten minutes), people either ate or walked along the platform in pyjamas.

In general, Siberia presented an image of poverty, at least as far as we could see from the train. Once I remember that, through a window, I saw a meeting being held at the station. Someone was reading from a manuscript and all the others looked bored, as probably they are at all the meetings in Poland.

Finally we came to the border of China. There the train was to stand six hours before crossing the frontier. We were afraid it would be boring, but a car from China awaited us and, instead of spending the time at the Soviet station, we visited the Chinese border town of Manchuli. There we met a young Chinese Ph.D., a former student of Professor Born,[22] who accompanied us on our trip through China.

The border town was small but it was scrupulously clean. I was delighted with its character and with the colourful people—mainly elderly—dressed in folk style. The men had grey beards and the women walked with difficulty on feet that had been bound according to a fashion prevailing fifty years earlier. I saw few young people. There were a few boys, in blue drill uniforms, and girls dressed like the boys, in the same uniforms which I was to see later on all the officials, with this difference: the higher officials had theirs made of quality grey or black wool.

We rested in a small, neat hotel, took a walk, and then returned for dinner. I consider Chinese cooking to be the best in the world, even better than French. I remember only one dish, which was a speciality of that province—apples cooked in hot caramelized sugar.

Soon after we returned, our train moved, now with Chinese personnel who cleaned and polished without end. The view from the window changed to reveal a sun-drenched landscape. We had the impression of a country full of people. The hills and mountains were denuded of trees, and their baldness made a strange impression. The people wore conical Chinese hats and blue cotton clothes as they gathered rice. The small huts of mud and clay looked extremely clean. Train conductors enthusiastically swatted the flies that had come with us across the Soviet-Chinese border. In China we saw not a single one. This is evidence not only of the love of cleanliness but also of the nation's great discipline. When the order came to kill flies, not a single person ignored it. I also remember that, when I later looked out of the window of the New Peking Hotel on the many cars standing in the yard, I saw how all the drivers cleaned them without end. The same was true during trips by train—continual cleaning. And endless serving of green tea which took the place of water.

I asked our companion whether one should tip. He told me that anyone offered a tip would be insulted. I myself saw how a waiter came to the dining car several times to ask who had left five yuan, so that he could return them. In purchasing power, five yuan is roughly equivalent to an English pound.

Poland

After two days' travel we arrived in Peking. I have the impression that there are three cities for which one yearns forever after having seen them—Rome, Paris, and Peking. Peking is surrounded by a wall beyond which is found the new city. There, hundreds of schools and centres of science and administration are being built. These are large buildings still retaining something of their Chinese character, mainly through the use of curved green roofs.

The old, wall-enclosed city, already surrounded by the new tall buildings, was composed of low houses and gardens within walls. The emperor had passed a law that no one could build a house taller than his palace. They say that one man did, and as a result lost his head. Within the walls that line the streets were houses decorated with lanterns and well-kept flowers and bushes. Everything shone with cleanliness. The Forbidden City was the emperor's palace, composed of hundreds of separate houses. Apparently every concubine—and there were hundreds of them—had her own house with its garden. All this, surrounded by its walls, was once inaccessible to ordinary mortals, but is now a public park and museum. The most important building is the T'ien an Men, guarded by bronze lions, opening on the street. From the balcony, dignitaries review the parade on the national holiday of October first.

Which of the things I saw seemed to me most remarkable? I saw factories, schools, universities, palaces, museums, but most interesting of all remained the Chinese themselves. I had no idea that a nation can be so disciplined. Everyone killed flies when told to do so. Everyone did gymnastics at a fixed hour, all the prices in all the shops (at that time many of them were private) were exactly the same; everyone gave a receipt for the exact amount of his sales, for the tax record; everyone talked in the same clichés and argued in the same way. This uniformity did make a monotonous impression, but also exuded a tremendous feeling of strength. Unfortunately, it was not so easy to penetrate behind the exterior. The Polish writer Antoni Słonimski described wittily, though no doubt exaggeratedly, his conversation with a Chinese poet who was in Warsaw.

"What kind of verse do you write?" asked the Chinese poet. Słonimski answered: "Various kinds—long and short."

"We also write long and short verse," answered the Chinese poet, smiling broadly.

The wife of Minister Żółkiewski told me of her conversation with the Chinese Minister of Education when he was in Poland.

"Poles are very polite and hospitable."

"The Chinese are also very hospitable."

"But the Poles are more hospitable," answered the Chinese Minister.

"No, the Chinese are more hospitable."

And so on, round and round.

Sometimes it is possible to penetrate behind the exterior. I had been given the address of a Chinese who had spent some time in Europe. He spoke in a completely open manner, using even such terms as, "He's an idiot, he's a swine, that one has no influence at all, but rather has a swelled head." He talked in the style so often used in Warsaw cafés. He was the only one of this type I met.

The uniformity of conversation, the contacts with people, would have been tiring if it had not been for the great courtesy and the truly great attention we were accorded as guests. Let me give one example. I took with me to China only a raincoat, because I knew that it would be warm there in October. The Chinese, however, felt I would be very cold on the trip back through Siberia in November, and they insisted upon making a winter coat for me. They bought the material, sent for a tailor and paid the bill. To this day I have the coat.

The streets were full of people. In the shops, colourful with signs in the beautiful Chinese characters, it was possible to find everything. They say that, formerly, one could have reduced the price to one-fifth by bargaining. But now the prices were fixed in all shops. The State Department Store had excellent goods, fine materials, and they were relatively inexpensive. The means of transport included tramways, of which there were few in Peking, and autos in which the dignitaries rode; but the most common means consisted of bicycle pedicars, which replaced the old rickshaws.

We came in time for the big holiday of October first. On September 30, there was a huge banquet in the Peking Hotel for two thousand people. I was one of these, and, since the Chinese convinced themselves that I am a distinguished scholar and scholars are much respected there, my place at the table followed Chou En-lai and [Pietro] Nenni. Chou En-lai has an alert look exuding strength and determination. After the toasts, which were translated into English, Russian, and

French, Chou En-lai got up and clinked his glass in turn with each of the two thousand people present in the two great halls of the Peking Hotel.

The next day there was the parade. We received an invitation and badges giving us places from which, as guests, we were to observe. They were in the same stand as Nenni, [Jean-Paul] Sartre, and Simone de Beauvoir. The parade began punctually at the hour announced: Chou En-lai and other state dignitaries appeared on the balcony of the T'ien an Men. There, for the first time, I saw Mao Tse-tung, dressed like all the others in the national uniform of grey. The parade itself was fantastically colourful. It began with a military review of the newly named marshals in new uniforms. The civilians, furthermore, showed a discipline as precise as the military. The whole performance was directed with great care and without incident. The marchers carried flowers, doves, balloons, portraits of their leaders, dragons, and performed sports and juggled as they passed the tribune. In the evening, there was a reception at which I met Mao Tse-tung. We exchanged a few words. His soft face and the soft manner in which he gave his hand made the impression of a thinker, a university professor, rather than a statesman. From the balcony we watched the singing and dancing people of Peking and the splendid Chinese fireworks.

I spent a month in China. Remembering it now, eight years later, the whole time seems to me like one night's dream. I saw much during that month—beautiful Peking with its old Forbidden City of eight hundred palaces, some of which are today museums showing the treasures that were not stolen; Shanghai, formerly a city of exploitation, where we lived in the rich French hotel that previously Chinese could enter only through the servants' entrance. We rested at Lake Hanchou, charmingly placed in the hills; we went to Nanking and the grave of Sun Yat-sen, creator of the Chinese republic; we saw the Dowager Empress's Summer Palace built with the funds intended for the Chinese fleet, the Peking opera loud and with acrobatics, in which men play women's roles and the costumes are rich and colourful; we saw the Shanghai opera where women play the parts of men, quieter and more melodious, and many institutes, schools, nursery schools, cooperative farms, and private apartments.

In going to China I did not feel that I was going to an unknown country. During the war some Chinese students had come to study in Toronto. One of them not only was my student but became a true friend as well. He often visited us in the evening and told us fascinating tales about his country. Here is an example of his extraordinary enthusiasm and industry. During a discussion one evening there emerged an idea for calculating a radar problem on which we were working together. After he left I went to sleep. The next morning my Chinese friend came to me with twenty pages of beautifully written calculations on which he had worked the whole night.[23]

Before this time, when I was in Princeton, I had become friendly with another theoretical physicist from China. During my stay in the United States and Canada I had met several Chinese scholars, progressive people who later returned to their country, becoming important and honoured there. When I was in Peking my friend from Princeton was either president or dean of the university and my friend from Toronto was a dean.

The Polish ambassador told us much about the hospitality of the Chinese but he also remarked that they never invited foreigners into their homes. Neither he nor any other Pole had been so invited, but Helen and I were. The first to ask us was the Vice-President of the Academy of Sciences (the President explained that he could not because his wife was ill.)

The Vice-President's home for two people consisted of three small rooms, like everything else, shining clean. On the walls were unframed Chinese scroll pictures, the chairs were not comfortable, having neither arms nor backs, but they were beautifully carved. Supper consisted of about a dozen courses of such specialities as shark's fins, bird nest soup, and—the *pièce de résistance*—sea slugs, a dish served for especially honoured guests.

I also visited the home of my old friends from Toronto and Princeton. Everywhere was the same meticulous cleanliness, modest furnishings, Chinese scroll paintings on the walls, and quite extraordinary hospitality.

I gave a few lectures, mainly in Peking. I spoke English and our physicist-companion translated without any hesitation. I was surprised to find that often two sentences of mine were contained in three Chinese words. I have very little talent for languages and did not learn any

Chinese characters. My wife had with her an English book on Chinese and fared somewhat better, picking up a few characters.

In China I talked much with physicists. I had the impression that they were making the same mistake which had been made in Poland before 1950—spreading the existing number too thin. Not many people who are not themselves scientists understand how isolation destroys research. And this applies to every field. Take Poland, for example. In Łódź and Lublin theoretical physics is practically non-existent. But it does exist in Warsaw and other centers. What should be done so that theoretical physics may be spread over all of Poland? From time to time, someone from the Ministry of Higher Education wrings has hands and has an inspiration: we must send Mr. X from Warsaw to Łódź and Mr. Y to Lublin. What would be the result of such an action? Warsaw would lose Messrs X and Y but there are other physicists there and Warsaw can get along without those two. But something worse would happen. Messrs X and Y would be lost to research. They would find themselves in a barren centre without scientific stimulation. In isolation their inspiration would die. There is, however, a way to have theoretical physicists in Łódź and in Lublin. Let us suppose that, in Łódź, there are two talented young students of physics, and in Lublin one. Give them scholarships to Warsaw. They will be trained in the Warsaw school. Then they can return to their cities, followed by others in the same way and, slowly, a strong school of theoretical physics will grow up in each of these cities, one capable of developing independently.

The same danger threatening individual scientists working alone also threatens a centre that has no contact with other centres. Science, to use an outworn phrase, is international. We learn a hundred times as well through direct contact or through preprints, through information telling us what our colleagues are working on, by inviting them to come to us and by sending our people to foreign scientific centres, than by merely reading articles, sometimes outdated by the time they are published.

Let us return to the Chinese. They had not been able to overcome these two dangers. There were but few scientists and those had mostly been trained abroad in a haphazard way. Many new universities were opened, and the scholars were spread over them in such a thin layer that, in nearly every one of the centres, there was one theoretical

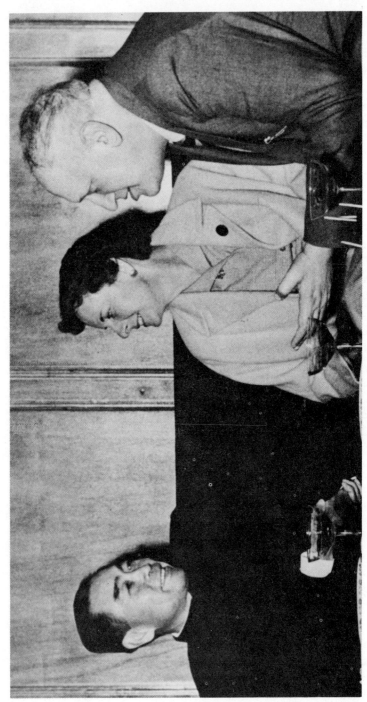

PLATE 7. The Infelds with Chou En-lai in Peking 1955.

physicist who could teach his students the outdated concepts that he had once learned. There was no chance to do research.

China made use of Soviet scientific aid. But instead of sending her highest-level scholars there for further study, China sent secondary school graduates for a few years' training—mainly in engineering.

I had a fairly long talk with Chou En-lai on this subject. He understood my point very quickly. We talked through a translator—I in English, the translator in Chinese, Chou En-lai in Chinese, and the translator again in English. Finally, when we were saying goodbye, Chou En-lai turned to my wife and said in perfect English, smiling, "Your chief duty is to take care of your husband's health."

The end of my connection with China is not without irony. Soon after my visit Chou En-lai was a guest of Poland, and the Chinese Ambassador arranged a banquet in his honour, to which I was not invited. On the day of the banquet, there was sudden activity. They tried to telephone me at home and at the institute and very warmly asked my wife and me to come that evening, since the distinguished guest himself had asked for me. It turned out that the Ambassador had forgotten me, but not Chou En-lai. At the reception a member of the embassy staff came and told us that Chou En-lai would like to see us, and had invited us to the head table. There he greeted me warmly and said that I should come to China every year for six months. We drank each other's health with the Chinese word "kampei."

In 1955, not long after Einstein's death, I received a letter from Bertrand Russell. It included an appeal, addressed to the two greatest powers, against the arms race and for peace; this Einstein had signed before he died. I considered that in the essentials it was a proper appeal, and I added my name despite some small reservations. Later I learned that, besides Einstein and Russell, among the signatures were those of a number of Nobel Prize winners including Linus Pauling, Frédéric Joliot-Curie, and Max Born. Among the more than a dozen signatories, only two were not Nobel Prize winners. One of these was Professor Joseph Rotblat of London—born and educated in Poland, the former student of the best Polish physicist of the inter-war years, Professor [Ludwik] Wertenstein. Professor Rotblat is now the secretary-general and the pillar of the Pugwash movement that arose out of the Einstein-Russell appeal. The second non-Nobel prize winner was myself.[24]

My interest in the question of nuclear war began with my time in Canada. It is even possible that the real reason for the attack on me was my activity on behalf of peace. In Poland, work for this cause brought with it only honour. I was (in fact I still am, although not active) a member of the World Peace Movement and served on its praesidium. Yet to bring into this movement non-leftists who longed for peace (and undoubtedly they exist!) proved very difficult if not impossible.

As long as Joliot was alive, I always found it most pleasant to talk with this great and charming physicist at praesidium or Council meetings. Also pleasant was the continued contact with Professor Bernal. Besides these two (now only one), the members were mainly humanists. My influence on the course of the meetings was minimal. The World Peace Movement was pretty well ignored by the Western world and listened to mainly in the socialist countries.

The Pugwash conferences were quite different. They were generally small—about seventy people were invited. The first of these I attended was at Kitzbühel in 1958. Initially, the relation between the Soviet and American scientists was full of distrust and serious doubts. However, scientists quickly understand one another and easily reach compromises. The atmosphere of mutual suspicion evaporated day by day, and in the end there was friendship. If I played some role in this meeting it was because I know both worlds—the East and the West—better than others do.

The closing ceremony of the conference was held in Vienna. The President of Austria invited us to a lunch at the Burg, and, in the evening, there was a gala performance at the opera (for me a bore). In addition there were two meetings. One was public and held in the largest hall in Vienna. Its chairman was the Foreign Minister of Austria, and ten scientists spoke. The reports were fairly academic in tone, and ten thousand listeners, together with the President of Austria, were somewhat bored. I was the tenth to speak. The platform was well lighted, and the hall was set in semi-darkness. I felt it strange to speak to people I could not see. There was only a sea of heads. I wanted to explain the disproportion between technical advances on the one hand and the lack of real progress on the other hand, in international relations. Here is a short excerpt from this ten-minute talk delivered in German:

> I was born in Krakow, in the days when that beautiful city belonged to the Austro-Hungarian Empire. When I was still a child, my father took me to Vienna in the year when Emperor Franz Joseph celebrated the sixtieth year of his reign. The trip from Krakow to Vienna then took—I well remember—seven hours. That was fifty years ago. Since then there has been an unprecedented advance in science and technology that could not then be anticipated. But what is the result of this advance for the citizens of Krakow who today want to travel to Vienna? The trip lasts at least twice as long as it did fifty years ago!

I was amazed at the unexpected and spontaneous enthusiasm of the audience. There was no end to the applause. It was my greatest triumph as a speaker. Why? It was the reference to the old Austro-Hungarian Empire and Emperor Franz Joseph that moved them so. Once awakened, the audience listened attentively and rewarded nearly every sentence with applause.[25]

The other meeting, more intimate, took place the same day in a room seating about two hundred people. Our long resolution from Kitzbühel was presented. There were also short speeches. Bertrand Russell came to Vienna. After the deaths of Einstein and Bohr I consider him the greatest living man. I have seen him again twice and have had the honour of talking with him. If I am not mistaken he is now over ninety. He looks like an old eagle from whom long life has taken the toll of a few feathers.

One year ago, in 1962, at the large Pugwash Conference in London, when those who had first signed the Einstein-Russell appeal sat at the speaker's table (we were then eight), Russell delivered a short but beautiful speech and received an ovation.

Only at the London and Vienna meetings did I hear Russell speak. He is the honorary president of the Pugwash movement. His place at conferences is usually taken by Professor [Cecil Frank] Powell, a Nobel prize winner, a most charming man who will not, I hope, mind if I call him my friend.

I was very glad when the London meeting chose me as the representative of the East European countries to the executive committee.

PLATE 8. The Infelds with Cecil Powell (left) and Joseph Rotblat at the Pugwash Conference in Prague 1964.

Perhaps it will be interesting to recount the origin of the name Pugwash. The Canadian millionaire, Cyrus Eaton—a man who is liberal, not only for a millionaire—invited those who had signed the Appeal and a number of other scientists to meet at his farm in Pugwash, Nova Scotia. There the organization was formed.

The significance of Pugwash continues to grow. To its meetings come advisers of Khrushchev and of the President of the United States. Their talks helped bring about the Moscow Partial Test Ban and at least some of the warmer atmosphere in international relations. This work would not seem to be without value.

The year 1956 was the memorable year of the Twentieth Congress and the Polish October changes. What effect did these have on science and on my life?

In May of that year, there was a general meeting of the Academy to elect new officers. We freely criticized the past, and my part in the discussion was not at all the most radical. I prepared my remarks carefully, and, later, they appeared in the Academy report and in the weekly *Przegląd Kulturalny* [*Cultural Review*]. I give here exerpts from my long speech:

> The purpose of my talk is not criticism for the sake of criticism. Collecting past mistakes for their own sake is a barren task. Only by means of open and frank discussion of mistakes can we expunge the bitterness collected in the hearts and minds of many of us. Only in this way can we break down the wall that stands between many scientists and the socialist system we want to build together. . . .
>
> Our friendship with the Soviet Union is a matter of great importance from the point of view of economics, the maintenance of peace, and the development of science. These things are known and recognized in Poland. But they did a disservice to this friendship who proclaimed that Russia was first in every important idea, large and small. Their insistence made Soviet science seem ridiculous, though in fact, and without their bullying, it holds a foremost place in the world. Those in our country who took up this Soviet bullying, adding their own to it, these people did a great disservice to Polish-Soviet friendship. How often young people have come to me with the question: are Mendeleyev and Pavlov really good scientists? This is the result of quoting Butlerov and Fiororov instead of Einstein in an article on space and time, or assigning the famous equation $E = mc^2$ not to Einstein but to Lebedev and

Vasilev in the Soviet philosophical dictionary.[26] By the way, this dictionary was translated into Polish and our graduate students unfortunately used it. . . .

One more memory from that time. I recall the session organized by the Academy after Stalin's death and dedicated to his achievements. A physicist took the floor and came out against Einstein, Bohr, and Dirac as "idealists." Professor Pieńkowski, who sat next to me, whispered in my ear: "Idealist physics can't be so bad if it produces people of that stature!" In fact, the speaker's attack had little if anything to do with a defence of the Marxist position. He used arguments quoted from certain passages of Marx and Engels. These creators of dialectical materialism could hardly be expected to forsee the development of physics in the twentieth century, so different from that of the nineteenth.

This period is ending, we hope forever. The Soviet Union is now passing through a period of renaissance in physics because the shackles binding it have been broken. Freedom has been returned to Soviet science. Cooperation with other countries is becoming more and more open. For me, the symbol of Soviet science is [Vladimir Yosifovich] Weksler's ten *Bev* syncophasatron, the largest technical advance in the science of our time. We hope that this renaissance will also come to Poland.

It is high time that the praesidum put its hands directly on the steering wheel and no longer remain, as it has been until now, merely a rubber-stamp for the secretariat. We must fight for the democratization of our organization. We must fight against secrecy in science where it only serves to cover ignorance. We must fight to let science be under the control of scientists and not the administrators who do not understand its needs. We must fight to train new experts, especially in those fields where there are few. We must fight against insincerity and cant, of which we have heard much. We must fight for a renaissance of scientific thought so that there can be no return to darkness, on the verge of which we have been for five years. We must fight for the honour and the future of Polish science.[27]

Then came October 1956. People were drunk with the freedom they had achieved. Some even changed it into licence. They say that, in Walbrzych, hoodlums beat up Jews. Then, when the Polish frontier was opened, many Jews left for Israel. It was even said that I was going. At first I took this gossip lightly, but then I heard it more and more often. One of my wife's fellow-workers even talked with someone who insisted that he had seen our passports. Another person told a professor I know that he had seen my trunk packed. When I was in Switzerland, Professor Pauli told me that his former student, a professor in Jerusalem, assured him that I was to come to Israel. Friends in Canada wrote that they had heard on the radio that we were to return there. A good friend in Paris heard that I would come to France to live. Someone else who visited China told me that he heard, in that far-off country, that I was going to Australia.

A reason was even offered for my leaving Poland. Allegedly, at one of my lectures (in one version this was in Warsaw, in another in Wrocław, and still another in Krakow), there was an anti-Semitic demonstration.

People thought there must be something in this gossip. After all, they say, where there's smoke there must be fire. How much was there in it really? Absolutely zero. Neither smoke nor fire. And since the story was made up out of whole cloth, someone must have made it. Who and for what reason?

There seem to be two alternatives. The gossip may have originated among the reactionaries. They would say "Look at Mr. I., to whom Poland has given everything. Look how Jews show their gratitude! If they get the chance they want to leave Poland!" Or the gossip may have originated among the Jews. "You blame us because we leave Poland? But Mr. I. was treated better than we, and he's also leaving." I don't know from which circle the gossip originated. Perhaps from both.

As the passage of time revealed that I was not leaving Poland, new gossip arose, which I heard several times. According to one version, [Josef] Cyrankiewicz, according to another Gomułka, and according to still another both of them, had asked me not to leave my country.

One thing emerges from this story—that Poland is the most rumour-mongering country in the world, and one in which there can be smoke without fire.

In May 1959 I went to Stockholm to attend a congress of the World Peace Movement, accompanied by the Polish delegation and my secretary. (Ever since my health began to fail, either my wife, my doctor, or my secretary always accompanied me.) One Saturday evening, when I went to bed, my head ached. In the morning after I awoke

PLATE 9. P. A. M. Dirac, Andrzej Trautman, and Leopold Infeld at the International Gravitational Conference 1962.

I had some difficulty in talking when ordering breakfast. My secretary, to whom I then telephoned, said that I had probably slept too little and that it would pass in a few hours. I was very eager that this be the case, because I was to go from Stockholm to Moscow for the Association of Scientific Workers; Khrushchev was to receive us. And so I dressed, though it was not easy, and went to lunch with my secretary. But it was difficult to move my right leg. I remember the strange feeling when I took a glass of milk in my right hand. I returned to my room, lay down, and asked my secretary to call a doctor. In Stockholm on a Sunday, it is not so easy to locate one. At last at six in the evening a doctor came. His diagnosis (or so they told me) was that I was simply tired and that it would soon pass. Later a Chinese doctor came, sent by Kuo Mo-zo.[28] He said it was probably a small stroke. (I had had something like it several years before, but much slighter. It had been accompanied by difficulty in talking.)

From the doctor I obtained a strong sleeping pill. In the morning I felt much worse. My worried secretary telephoned to the embassy, and also arranged that an ambulance would take me to the hospital where I had a private room and doctor's care. It was difficult for me to communicate with the doctors, not for lack of a common language but because I had difficulty in moving my tongue. In place of well-rounded words I produced a gurgle. On Wednesday, Helen came from Poland after receiving both passport and visa in one day. Every day I felt worse. First two fingers refused to work, then three, then my whole hand, until my whole right side was paralyzed. Psychologically I didn't feel badly, chiefly because my wife was there and I received wonderful care in the hospital. Before Helen came it was painful to think of dying far from my country, far from my children, whose photographs I had before me. In the early weeks of my illness, she was with me all day, and her presence brightened the hospital room. They told her that if I lasted through the first ten days then I was expected to live.

During the preceding few years I had been writing the book *Motion and Relativity* with one of my docents. My assistant's departure on a Rockefeller Fellowship had required that I finish it. Just before my illness, I was trying to understand the problem of motion of a spinning body in a gravitational field, on which several of my Ph.D. students were working.

While I lay motionless in the hospital I began to think again about this problem. Since I could not write I had to mumble to my wife, the only one who could understand me, and dictate the results of my thinking. I wanted to explain to her how to write the Christoffel symbol;[29] I took the pencil in my fist, with difficulty began to move it, and with difficulty drew the symbol on the whole page. Helen understood how important it was for me to know that I could still think, and she didn't prevent me.

In my life I have been in Canadian, English, Polish, and Swedish hospitals. The one in Stockholm was incomparably the best. My name meant nothing there, no tips were accepted, and yet the care was wonderful. The nurses—pretty young girls—showed kindness, a sense of responsibility, I should say even warmth. The hospital food was good, but I had no appetite and the chief nurse prepared special dinners for me. We became so friendly with her that we later invited her to visit us in Warsaw. The doctor brought a bottle of wine to strengthen me.

My condition slowly began to improve. I began to regain power in my hands, my speech improved, and finally there only remained (and unfortunately still remains) some weakness in the use of my right leg. Every day I had therapeutic gymnastics; I learned to walk, moved my fingers, all under the supervision of excellent nurses.

Professors from the university and polytechnical institute of Stockholm came to see me. Generally, in the whole time I was there, I experienced much kindness and not one unpleasantness. When I could take several steps after six weeks in the hospital, I was permitted to return to Warsaw. The children waited for me at the airport and were shocked to see their father carried on a stretcher from the plane to an ambulance.

In Warsaw, my health continued to improve. I could move and speak more and more easily. I spent the vacation period in Nieborów and, by the beginning of the academic year 1959–60, I was already working, although much less intensively than before. I was happy that my son obtained a stipend for Cambridge, that I was still alive, and that I had given the publisher *Motion and Relativity*, a book that had cost so much effort.[30]

But soon afterward there was new trouble. I was surprised that it was so difficult for me to breathe during the day. I thought that I probably had asthma. After a serious attack I called a doctor who said that it was caused by a weak heart. Despite the injections of strephantine the attacks returned in different intensities. Mainly they came at night. First fear, difficulty in breathing. Then came the attack. I changed my position from lying to sitting. I coughed in an effort to eject the liquid from my lungs. The cough intensified the feeling of difficulty in breathing. I coughed some more until I felt that I was choking. During an interlude I would gasp for a little air and then again there would be an attack of choking. That is how the attacks were. Between them there was difficulty in breathing. I could only pant. All the time I felt the existence of my lungs and that they were full of water. It was horrible. It was not worth while to live this way.

Later Wikta told me (she has a sharp medical eye) that she thought I would not live beyond March 1960. She said wherever she could and to anyone who might be able to help that only a medical virtuoso could save me. She proposed that Professor Paul Wood of London see me. After my worst attack he was brought in February. (It was during that last attack that I had to reassure the doctor who came to see me in the night that I did not intend to die just then.)

Professor Wood came on a Saturday afternoon and left again on Monday. For the first time I saw a doctor who thought completely logically and directly like a scientist. He told Helen that the unexpected could, of course, happen, but he believed that, within a week, he would have me out of the state I was in. From the time of his visit, the difficulty in breathing left me. I now work, grow old normally, and have even been abroad many times.

During the summer vacation of 1959 I not only lost the chance to see Khrushchev. In July there was a conference on gravitation near Paris which I was to have attended. My former students took my place.

The next conference on gravitation occurred in Poland at the end of July, 1962. Unfortunately I could not take such an active part in it as I would have liked, but my students helped me very much in organizing it. The conference was a success for Polish science. To Warsaw came professors Synge, Dirac, my old friend B[anesh] Hoffmann, and my former student from Toronto, A. Schild. The meetings were mainly in Jabłonna, a rebuilt palace near Warsaw, and in Warsaw itself. When I returned from one of the meetings in Jabłonna, my son found the notice of Professor Paul Wood's death

PLATE 10. Leopold Infeld with Hermann Bondi at the International Gravitational Conference 1962.

in the London *Times*. He was about ten years younger than I. He saved others, he saved me, but he did not want to or could not save himself. He died of a heart attack.

With this I conclude my account. In my private life during 1963 there has been, fortunately, little trouble, some happiness, mainly resulting from the good functioning of the institute. The only thing is that I grew a year older. I am now near the end of this journey. I am not afraid of death, but only of the act of dying. I should like it to be as painless as possible. I should also like my family and friends to avoid the funeral formalities that are barbarous in modern times. I hate to think that one of my former students will memorize a speech before a mirror to say at my funeral. I have told my wife not to allow any speeches or flowers. Both are quite unnecessary for the corpse. As is a black dress hurriedly made for the occasion. I am glad that, in my case, my wife will try to reduce these formalities to a minimum. And I am glad that I shall not have to see or criticize them.

While little has happened in my life in 1963, much has happened in the world. First there was the signing of the Moscow Partial Test Ban Agreement. It appeared that there may be a chance of really ending the cold war.

In September of 1963, I attended a Pugwash conference in Dubrovnik, Yugoslavia. The sky was blue, the sea warm and calm. In Dubrovnik the magic beauty of the Renaissance slumbers for five centuries. It was equally equitable in the meeting rooms. I felt convinced that the world was entering the era of peace.

These concluding words I write in Poland in November, 1963. I write them after the shocking news of Kennedy's murder. This assassination and its accompanying events show how fragile is man's foresight. I do not know whether we are entering an era of cooperation or a new Middle Ages. I do not know whether my children will live in a better world than the one in which I spent most of my life, or in a world of blood and storm. I do not know whether they will live in a world where freedom and prosperity will increase or decrease.

I do not know. But in the long run I believe that the path which zigzags from hilltop to valley leads upward. But what will the world be for my children Eric and Joan? I do not know.

Sketches
from the
past

Władysław Natanson

In 1964 the Jagiellonian University celebrated the six hundredth anniversary of its founding. Let us go back fifty years. At that time, in the Philosophical Faculty, there was only one mathematician, one professor of experimental physics and one of theoretical physics. There were no assistants in mathematics or theoretical physics, there were no seminars. I well remember the lectures in mathematical analysis given by Professor [Stanisław] Zaremba, a fine mathematician whose works, so the story goes, were presented in the Paris Academy of Sciences by Henri Poincaré himself. In 1917, Zaremba's lectures were attended by three students at most—a woman who sometimes appeared and sometimes not, a clever student who later committed suicide, and me. I completed the course as the only one of my year—both the best and the worst. Poland's greatest physicist, Professor Marian Smoluchowski, died suddenly during the vacation period after my first year. There remained only Władysław Natanson, my professor of theoretical physics.

After Smoluchowski's death his position was taken by Professor [Konstanty] Zakrzewski from Lwów. For nearly the whole period of my studies professors Zakrzewski and Natanson were the only professors of physics in the university. There were no younger ones. More —Professor Natanson had no assistants, and so during the whole period of my studies there were no exercise hours, no seminars, only lectures. For a short period—as I remember just before my doctoral exams in 1921—Professor Czesław Białobrzeski, who shortly thereafter went to Warsaw, was on the staff.

Professor Natanson lectured for five hours a week, from Monday to Friday, for the period that started at eleven-fifteen and ended at twelve. He always began at exactly twenty minutes after eleven—so punctually that one could set a watch by his arrival in the lecture room, and ended punctually at twelve. His lectures were always carefully planned in advance as an integrated whole, like a work of art, and were delivered without notes. He was always dressed ceremoniously, always the same—a morning coat such as Englishmen still wear in the daytime if invited to Buckingham Palace, a stiff collar, black tie, beautifully pressed striped trousers. We students often wondered how many identical outfits Professor Natanson must have at home. Before each lecture a cleaning-woman brought tea in a carafe from which he drank during the lecture. He spoke quietly, with a slight exaggeration, not so much in his voice as in the contents of the lecture. He wrote beautifully with a damp chalk on a damp blackboard—so beautifully that one wanted constantly to photograph the blackboard and hated to see the sponge erase the flourishes he had added to a Q or an H. In my life I have heard many splendid lectures but never any so technically perfect as Professor Natanson's.

His cycle of lectures lasted many years. I do not know how many because there was a change in the course of study. But they said that before my entrance to the university his cycle continued for seven or eight years. When I was in the first year, Professor Natanson lectured on thermodynamics (of course for the whole year). I attended these lectures a few times, fascinated by the beautiful form, the contents of which I understood nothing. Only in my second and third years did I regularly attend Professor Natanson's lectures. In my second year his subject was theoretical mechanics. I was particularly fortunate because I began his cycle at the beginning. I already knew the mechanics of the time from the books by Planck and Schaeffer.[1] Yet I listened with great interest to the original and fine lectures. I remember how, once, he brought with him Newton's *Principia*, put on his glasses and read to us in Latin, commenting as he went and drinking tea the while. I well remember the last lecture that year on mechanics. He dealt with the special theory of relativity, whose principles I learned then for the first time. Also for the first time I then heard the name of Einstein, whom Professor Natanson called the modern Copernicus and the genius among geniuses.

I have tried to evaluate what Professor Natanson gave me and what he did not give me as a physicist. He gave me the most important thing: the feeling for the beauty of theoretical physics. He aroused in me a love of the subject. For a very long time I was so much under the influence of Professor Natanson that I tried clumsily to imitate his manner of lecturing and his relation to people. Thus, for example, in Berlin, as a fifth-year student in Professor [Richard von] Mises's seminar, I wrote on a damp blackboard with damp chalk, and, consequently, probably no one was able to understand what I wrote. After reading my professor's popular articles I imitated his lovely baroque style in my own writing—no doubt with unfortunate results.

Yet I never had a single strictly nonscientific discussion with Professor Natanson. He was most polite, pleasant, and proper; and this very politeness kept me at a greater distance than would any gruffness. I remember, for instance, that I had difficulty understanding a subtlety in a lecture. I felt that it was not my fault—that something was not correct. It was the only time this happened during the whole period of my studies with Professor Natanson. It was during my third year, entirely devoted to elasticity and hydromechanics. Professor Natanson asked me to write out my comments. I did so on two or three pages, referring to my notes and commenting on how I had understood the lecture. I took these carefully written pages to number 3 Studencka Street, the home of my professor. When I approached him after the next lecture, Professor Natanson invited me to come to his house. He told me that my comments were correct, that he vaguely remembered that he had not presented the matter well. Afterward we talked about something quite different—about books, England, and Cambridge, about nature and the difficulty of understanding its laws. Everything he said was beautifully phrased so that one could publish it exactly as he talked, though it was impersonal and cold.

How strange Krakow was then, and how different its studies from those of today! During my whole course I did not take a single written examination; only orals, and even they were not required. They were taken only by those students who were planning to apply for scholarships or who wanted to have closer contact with their professors. Indeed, in theoretical physics where there were no assistants, no exercise hours, no seminars, this was the only way to make closer contact with a professor. During my fifth year of study I went for a half year to Berlin and brought back with me my first piece of research, which I wanted to use for my doctor's thesis. Professor Natanson listened to me, at his home, with his usual politeness and kindness, and then told me that the work I had described to him in one sentence should be officially submitted to the dean's office. I could not imagine it possible to go to him later in order to ask what he thought of my work, or whether he had read it. Two weeks later, the janitor told me that he himself had taken the paper from Professor Natanson to Professor Zakrzewski. That aroused my interest in both their opinions. Nowadays the report on a paper is given orally, and students are informed officially whether or not it has been accepted. In Krakow I was never told officially. The janitor helped me by giving me both their secret reports to read. These were extremely warm and favourable.

I also well remember my two-hour examination for the doctorate. Professor Natanson asked his questions in beautiful form. He began with general ones, going deeper and deeper into the subject. The first dealt with the theory of oscillations. Next he went on to the equipartition of energy and other classical problems. From the theory of relativity, the subject of my thesis, there was not a single question.

Professor Natanson was, of course, my promoter. After the sacred words *spondeo et polliceor* had been uttered, I gave my hand in the prescribed order—to the rector, dean, promoter. Professor Natanson invited me to come and see him. Once again, during my visit, we talked of the outlook for science, of books, including Eddington's, which he had received from England,[2] and of many other matters very general in nature and far removed from our personal lives.

For the next few years I was a teacher in secondary schools, first in provincial towns and then in Warsaw. During this time I had very little contact with Professor Natanson. I did not even know whether he remembered his student. For me he was an unseen and unattainable ideal, a god from Olympus. I devoured his articles which then appeared in book form. I recall how often, with tears in my eyes, I read his memoirs of Potkański and Smoluchowski—memoirs full of a feeling of loneliness and a longing for death. My professor never knew and never learned of the admiration I felt for him.

During the time I was in Warsaw my first papers appeared—first on education, later on scientific subjects. I sent them to my former professor. At once I received an answer. It was Professor Natanson's custom to reply to all letters on the day he received them. Unfortunately, I never learned this virtue from him. His letters were written in a beautiful hand, clear and large, and were in such fine style that they could have been printed just as they were. I deeply regret that of the many letters I received, I no longer have a single one.

These letters usually contained a few sentences about my latest research or some words of encouragement, always accompanied by reprints of his own scientific and popular work. While I read much of Professor Natanson's popular writings, I was well acquainted with only a few of his scientific papers. One that I studied carefully was his splendid monograph on radiation in a volume of the journal *Prace Matematyczno-Fizyczne* [3] which was issued in memory of August Witkowski. Besides this, I owned, and still own, his beautifully written but outdated *Introduction to Theoretical Physics*. [4]

During the eight years of my school-teaching, I saw my professor only twice, and, as I remember, only during the years when I returned to scientific work after a long break. In the school where I taught, my pupils used the textbook written by professors Natanson and Zakrzewski. [5] At the time, I thought it was exceptionally well written, though in a baroque style. It was obviously a book by someone who thought deeply about the basic principles of physics—no doubt too deeply for school pupils. It was seldom used in school. It should be reexamined to determine whether it could be saved and adjusted for use today. I remember the lively introduction on the concept of work. It analysed this concept in a literary way, discussing its role in our lives. With what pleasure I read aloud those lofty phrases of my mentor, forgetting that young people are not impressed by expressions that are too lyrical! Once, when I met Professor Natanson during this period I told him that my pupils were using his text. He regretted that the book had cost him so much time, that together with his position as rector it had kept him from scientific work, that the years when he wrote it were difficult years. As I remember our talk today I marvel at his art of discussing personal matters in a completely detached way. Not a single personal remark fell from his lips. Our conversation turned about scientific problems, but it never dealt with people themselves.

As my own research developed, the influence of Professor Natanson naturally waned. I withdrew from him, and my adoration suddenly turned into distaste. Today I speak of this frankly because I know that I was unfair. I probably resented that he did not give me what he could not give—that he had not trained me in the technique of scientific work and had not given me the conditions for such work. I did not take into account that, at the time, there were probably only three centres in Europe for such training—with Sommerfeld, Bohr, and Born,[6] and that I met him during that period of life when one finds it difficult to change. His scientific career had bloomed during the times of Emperor Franz Joseph I, when there were only two universities which gave lectures in Polish: Krakow and Lwów. Krakow looked down on Lwów. Once Professor Natanson said to me: "If anyone in the world knows about Polish science, he knows only about Krakow science." Thus there was, in effect, one university that really meant something. And at that university, there was only one chair of theoretical physics. To attract students, to train them—this was looked upon in old Krakow as vulgar, smacking of the kindergarten. It was considered proper to select one student during a lifetime, make him a docent, and let him wait quietly for his professor to retire or die. In order that he might wait not too impatiently, he should be a person of some means, politically reliable—which meant a Krakow conservative—and be of good family. If such a person has already been found, then Pauli's exclusion principle applies: the place is filled and no one else can aspire to it. One should then discourage and frighten away any other candidates.

Perhaps what I have just written is an exaggeration. But not much. It was not surprising that when the Polish state was reestablished in 1918 there were not enough professors to fill the posts. For a long time there was no professor of theoretical physics in the University of Lwów. The choice for the position in theoretical physics in Poznań was a public scandal. Under such conditions—I see it clearly now—my attitude to Professor Natanson was not justified, for I did not take into account the conditions under which he lived and developed his scientific and literary talents.

After eight years of teaching in a secondary school I became an assistant in Lwów thanks to the efforts of Professor [Stanisław] Loria, and later I was "habilitated" at that university (a process by which one's research and personality are judged, making one potentially eligible for a future appointment as a professor). Professor Natanson assisted me in this process by his comments on my work. When I sent him my first popular science book *New Pathways of Science* [*Nowe Drogi Nauki*], I received by return post a beautiful letter from which it followed that he had already read the book. He spoke of it in flattering terms. I remember one sentence of the letter that accurately characterized modern physics: "Nowadays theories shrivel up and die more quickly than flowers." Later, when I sent him from Cambridge my joint work with Born, in which there was a new constant called b,[7] I received a letter from which again I remember one sentence: "Your b has penetrated deep into my soul."

From Cambridge I returned to Krakow for a meeting. I was glad that I would see Professor Natanson, that he would attend my lecture about my work with Born. But unfortunately he was ill. I went to see him at his home, where we talked about Cambridge. He was distressed that they had cut the ivy from the famous Trinity College gate. He was always full of charm, and our talk this time was, as always, impersonal. This was the last time I saw him. When I was at Princeton, in 1937, I received the news of his death.

Today I can better judge the complicated character of my professor. I realize that he was incapable of intrigue, knightly and noble, brought up in comfort, dreading contact with life, with its brutality and in-difference. He was lonely both in science and in life, and the im-personality in his relations with people was his protective armour. Such an armour, too, was his great politeness, which was so extreme as to embarrass. In science he was near, very near, to great discoveries—for example, the formulation of [S. N.] Bose's statistics.[8] As a result of his isolation, his lack of personal contact, he did not develop to his full scientific capacity. However, he did develop to the full his talent for writing. He did not have students but he had an influence on the national culture. During the first years of this century, he was the only theoretical physicist in Poland. The history of theoretical physics in this country begins with Professor Natanson. Now, a quarter of a century after his death, we have many young scientists who continue the work begun by him. There is no fear that theoretical physics will die out in Poland. It must remain close to the world trend and free of dogmatic errors. From the life and works of Professor Natanson young scientists can learn much—a humanitarian approach to science, elegant formulation of ideas, respect for scientific work, modesty, and understanding that in science we try awkwardly to reflect the beauty of nature as well as to aid mankind.

Bronia

Krakowska Street was the main street of the Jewish district of Krakow. Most of the buildings here were owned by Jews, and the tenants, besides the janitors, were also Jews. But there were a few exceptions. Such a one was the house at number 9—old, two-story, owned by old Mrs. Wojcikiewicz and her son, who lived in the house and were treated like a royal family.

On the ground floor was a shop serving mead—a shop recalled in his stories by the Krakow writer M[ichał] Bałucki. One flight up lived the Wojcikiewiczes and Dr. Jungier, the best physician in the district of Kazimierz. On the second floor lived Salomon Infeld and his family. Dr. Jungier was bald, small, spoke Polish badly, but as a doctor he had the divine gift. When he first visited us, he took a crown and, later, a whole gulden. When he came to me he always asked a stereotyped question: "You had a muffment? Dere's gas?"

The Infeld family consisted of the parents, grandfather, two sisters, and me. Then there was the maid-of-all-work who slept in the kitchen on a primitive bed which was covered to form a big table in the daytime.

From the hallway on the right the door led into a large room in which the life of the Infelds was concentrated day and night. It served as the dining-room and a bedroom. Two iron bedsteads stood with their backs to the wall. In one slept my grandfather and in the other my two sisters—Bronia and Fela—and I slept in the sofa at right angles to the beds. My grandfather awoke every night between two and three o'clock, turned on the light, pulled up his nightshirt, searched for bedbugs, scratched himself, then pulled down his nightshirt and began his nightly wandering with a candle around the room. High up on the cupboard was a plate with his supper which he had not eaten when all the others had the meal. Now, at three in the morning, always in the same long underwear with black stripes, he reached for the plate. Every night I waited until his loud mastication should end and the candle be put out. When I was small, my grandfather often beat me with his black umbrella. Later, when I grew up, we always quarrelled. Throughout (he died when I was in Konin), there remained between us a great mutual dislike.

From the hallway, the door on the left led into what was called the salon and to my parents' bedroom. The door to the salon was kept locked and opened only for guests.

Fela, my sister who was three years older than I, was a red-head, pretty, pious, a good daughter and wife and also a good sister. Yet it was hard for us to find a common language.

Bronia, four years younger than I, was tall and blond. I found her beautiful, though I imagine that she was weak in sex-appeal. Lacking in personal ambition, she understood everyone and everything. While she lived she was my best and closest friend.

Each of us in turn—that is, Fela, I, and Bronia—went to the same commercial school. We were all good students but Bronia was exceptional. Her reports were boring because they only carried the mark "very good." She helped her poorer classmates and conducted for them a free course in mathematics and Polish. But the way to university was closed to graduates of the commercial school. At the best she could register for a teachers' course and receive a diploma entitling her to teach at an elementary school. She took such a course and was outstanding for her intelligence and ability.

Later, when I had completed my doctorate and became the director of the secondary school in Konin, Bronia came to me and took the position of an elementary school teacher. Even today, after forty years, the few still living who knew her in Konin remember her fine, sweet character. They remember her excellent demonstration lessons at the district conference. I recall how Bronia told me about her principal's advice that no one should go to class without ruler in hand and how distressed Bronia was by this idea. She well knew that the one way to keep discipline in class was to maintain interest.

While still teaching in Konin, Bronia became engaged to our cousin whom she later married. A number of young men were in love with her. But she chose a man exceptionally good and kind though not very successful or ambitious. Menashe, for that was his name, was a poorer edition of Bronia. A lawyer by training, he had a fine sense of humour, and tried his hand at a number of different jobs by which, during the difficult times between the two world wars, he supported his family. But the couple's financial hard times were never a cause for bad humour.

Menashe was the son of my father's brother and so Bronia did not need to change her name when she married. My father bought for the young couple a three-room apartment at 28 Królowej Jadwigi Street on the outskirts of the city, near the Jordan Park [playground] and Błonia. Their furniture was middle-class in style, but the atmosphere of their home was not at all bourgeois.

Every Friday evening young people, mainly communists, came together in Bronia's home, where they loved the feeling of freedom and gaiety. Today a few state dignitaries who were once part of this group recall with nostalgia those Friday evenings. One of them told me: "Such women as Bronia don't exist in the world now." The same man also recalled: "When Menashe had a good week financially then on Friday there was fish, and when he had a worse week, pickled herring. But what herring!"

Besides the communists, Bronia's guests included writers and scientists—people to whom the relaxed atmosphere, the sense of intellectual ease appealed.

The young Leon Kruczkowski who later became a well-known playwright and novelist was a guest at Bronia's, as were the Seidenbeutlow boys, twins, well-known painters before the Second World

War. Bair Horowitz, the Jewish poet, often came, and one Friday he brought along his friend, an exceptionally good magician. Today, after forty years, people tell me the details of this evening.

Among Bronia's guests were S[tefan] Rozental, now a professor of theoretical physics in Copenhagen, and Hertz Weber, the best student of Leon Chwistek, the logician, mathematician, and painter. Weber always brought Chwistek along with him whenever that Lwów professor was in Krakow. For each of her guests Bronia had a smile, pleasant words, and a sympathetic ear for their confidences, always trying to help them in their problems.

The apartment was beleaguered by beggars who came at all times of the day and night for a piece of bread and butter or alms. The beggars were many between the wars and were very well organized. They marked the gate to indicate at which apartments it was easy to get a handout. No doubt Bronia had a high place on this list.

I fell in love when I was sixteen and married when I was twenty; before I was thirty the meaning had gone out of my marriage. When I was considering divorce (we then lived in Warsaw) my wife returned to Krakow where her mother was. Only she did not stay with her mother, but with Bronia. Bronia, who always sympathized with the unhappy, also underwent this test of boredom and listened over and over to the same complaints of this unhappy woman against her own brother. I then received a letter from Bronia asking me to return to my wife. Later she told me that she could not resist the continued insistence. My wife was sure that the letter from my beloved sister would change my mind. But Bronia knew me well enough to realize, as she told me later, that the letter would have no effect on me.

After my divorce I married Halina, with whom I spent four happy years. She died before she was thirty, doomed by an incurable disease. During those four years, fate kept me away from Krakow. Yet I saw Bronia from time to time, and maintained constant contact by letter. I was always convinced that Bronia would survive me by many years. During our time together, Bronia was Halina's and my best friend.

Halina's death was the greatest tragedy of my life. Even now, after thirty years, it is hard for me to write about it. I had not the strength to return to my position in Lwów and I remained for several months in Warsaw, sunk in hopeless mourning. As soon as Bronia learned of Halina's death she sent a telegram giving the date and time of her arrival in Warsaw. For several weeks she left her husband, her child, her home, to help lighten my pain.

Wherever I was afterward, whether in England or the United States, I always received her good letters. I remember the last time we met, when I visited them before my departure for America. She was calm, as always, although she was worried by the friendship developing between Poland and Germany. I will never forget the long evening talks, the serene, relaxed atmosphere which prevailed at 28 Królowej Jadwigi Street. Their son was then very small, no more than four years old. He impressed me as very intelligent and sensitive. Romus, for that was his name, had decided that God did not exist. I remember his argument:

"How can God exist when the sailors on a ship obey their captain and still have accidents?" He sketched for me various machines he had invented. This was in 1936, the last year I was in Poland before the Second World War. After that I had only letters. Nothing remains except a brown tie that Bronia sent me in America when someone was going over. That tie, old and shabby, outlasts all the newer ones in my wardrobe.

What happened to Bronia after I went to America I learned partly from her letters and partly from what people told me in Poland. Romus was four years old and attended a nursery school. Unfortunately, Bronia's financial situation worsened. She had many friends who had finished their studies and were without work. It was not easy then to obtain a job in Poland. In Krakow there was one Jewish secondary school which was Zionist and rather reactionary. Why not start a progressive cooperative school? Thus Bronia took a remarkable decision. After a long search she found a place on Starowislana Street. Any university graduate who wanted to teach at this school had to contribute a thousand zlotys and engage not to expect pay for two years. I do not know where Bronia got her thousand zlotys. But she did start a very modern school that developed splendidly, that was well equipped and in its very first years offered strong competition to the existing Jewish secondary school. The war swept away the generations of teachers and pupils. Nothing remains of Bronia's work, or of my work as a teacher.

When I was in Canada during the war I worried about Bronia. I read in the paper that there was a way of saving the lives of Jewish children, that for a certain sum the Nazis would let them leave the country. I offered Bronia help and I remember the short letter I got in reply through the Red Cross, informing me that she did not want to be separated from her son. Later I learned that the Nazis extorted dollars from abroad in this way, at the same time ordering the children to be killed.

After the war I received a letter from my sister Fela's daughter, freed from the Bergen Belsen concentration camp. She wrote me that Fela, Bronia's husband Menashe, and their son Romus were dead. But it was possible that Bronia was still alive. And so I waited for news of her. Bronia did not look Jewish. She had naturally blond hair and smacked of the Polish countryside. But no news came. Only when I returned to Poland did I learn of Bronia's fate and her family's.

On the day before war began Bronia started out with her son to leave Krakow. Her husband had the rank of sergeant and was in the reserve army. At the time of mobilization his whole fortune amounted to twenty zlotys. I was later told how Menashe, always calm, tried to change the twenty-zloty bill.

Bronia certainly did not have strength enough to make her way with her seven-year-old son along roads jammed with wagons, trucks, cars, along which only people with sharp elbows could drive ahead. And so she returned to her apartment. Probably one of the very first orders issued by the Nazis was to evacuate the few Jews living in this district. The conspiratorial groups which manufactured false documents were not yet in full operation. Perhaps Bronia was afraid of being exposed by the owner of the building or by neighbours. I only know that she went with her husband to Tarnów.

While Bronia did not look Jewish, Menashe did, and his first and last names proclaimed his background. I have been told—I do not know whether or not it is true—that Romus clung to his mother and was ashamed of his father's Jewish appearance. One can hardly blame a boy, at most eight years old, for this. If it is true, then Bronia, attached as she was to her husband, must have felt indeed tragic.

One day on Tarnów Street a German soldier came up to Menashe and asked him a quite harmless question, something of the type: how do you go to such-and-such a street? Or perhaps it was: what time is it? Instead of answering quietly Menashe could not control his nerves and started to run away. The soldier shot the fleeing Menashe and killed him.

Such was the end of the best marriage I knew.

Bronia, as far as I know, was not a member of the Communist Party, but most of her friends were. I can imagine that during the occupation she would be careless of her own life and become more and more involved in conspiratorial work. After her husband's death she went to live in a mountain village resort near Krakow, called Maków.

On a certain day she was to go to Krakow to keep an appointment for a planned purpose. She never arrived and ever since all trace has disappeared. No one knows what happened. That was why my niece wrote that perhaps Bronia still lived. I believe that the most probable explanation is that the Nazis made a search on the train from Maków to Krakow, found either arms or forbidden literature on her, and killed her on the spot.

Fela's husband looked after Bronia's son and took him to Krakow. There Romus caught typhoid fever and was killed by the Nazi doctor in the hospital.

That was the end of Bronia and her family.

Why do I write about these sad experiences? It is only the death of three people and, in Poland, six million were lost. There are two reasons.

There are still in Poland many people who knew or were friends of Bronia. When they recall the period between the two world wars, they certainly think of the sweet and kind Bronia. She lives on in their memories. In my memory she will live as long as I do. I should like to introduce her into the memories of those who will read these words.

But there is a second reason. Perhaps this book may reach the hands of those who know the details of her life and death. As my own life nears its close I think more and more vividly about her tragic story.

Konin

Early in the summer of 1922, I had been a Ph.D. for exactly a year and had taught for two years in the provinces. I was almost twenty-four years old and was bursting with unsatisfied ambition. The Jagiellonian University, from which I had obtained my doctorate as the one and only student of Professor Natanson in the thirty-five years of his professorship, took no interest in my future. What remained open to me was to work in a Jewish school.

In the park that rings the old city of Krakow called the Planty, I met a former classmate. He told me that he was teaching history in a private school for Jewish pupils in Konin, that it was a *gimnasjum* [secondary school] where pupils were exceptionally intelligent and able, that although one could not yet reach the town by train there was a station already built and the railroad would come there any day, that they were looking for a new headmaster. He asked if I would not consider replacing him. If so, he would write to the school board offering my name and qualifications.

The plan appealed to me. In Krakow I had many former classmates and friends, either as young as or slightly older than I, who would be ready to take a position in the provinces to work with me. One of these was my good friend Szymon Ohrenstein, a splendid mathematician, a noble, modest, and charming man, who later was tortured to death by the gestapo.

Thus I took the position offered me as headmaster of the school with the hope that I could build up the best secondary school in Poland. On my staff were five Ph.D.s who had minimal or no experience as teachers but were full of enthusiasm and willingness to work. The pupils realized this, and we enjoyed their full confidence, I would even say their love.

In the autumn of 1922, it was already possible to go to Konin by train. But what sort of train? It was a local running between Kutno and Strzałkowa, at the great rate of twelve to twenty miles an hour. Some day it would be part of the connection between Warsaw and Poznań, when the rails were laid, or so they said. But this was the dream of the future. From the station it was a twenty-minute ride by droshky or cart to the town, which was nearly two miles from the station and situated picturesquely on the bank of the River Warta.

The coming of the railroad changed the face of the town, and the population began to shrink. Every month important citizens moved away to Bydgoszcz, Kalisz, or Kutno. At one time our school had had two hundred pupils, but that was in the former, blessed times. In 1922 the number had dropped to one hundred and twenty.

Formerly the school board had planned and had begun to build the best looking and largest building in Konin in order to house the *gimnasjum*. I was told that this new school would soon be ready. When I left Konin two years later the building was in more or less the same state. Despite much effort, I had been able to complete only two rooms on the ground floor of this three-story building.

I shall never forget a story connected with this building, which I repeat here for posterity to ponder.

The local reactionary fringe invited the master bricklayer for drinks and persuaded him to erect one wall without foundations. How funny it would be, thought those who invented this game, when one beautiful day the wall would collapse burying under it the Jewish children and their teachers!

But Jehova at that time looked out for his children. The wall, before it collapsed, began to buckle. The deception of the builder was discovered. He had to straighten the wall at his own cost and put a foundation under it.

I imagined that to be the headmaster of a school would be a wonderful thing. But clouds began to gather on the horizon. The Łódź school inspector, whose jurisdiction included our school, did not approve my appointment. The inspector told me sharply that I was too young, that twenty-four-year-old headmasters belonged only in operettas. The second difficulty was the financial situation, the growing pauperization of the middle class in Konin and the loss of population. To insist on some sort of possible conditions for teaching, we had to resort to a strike. In addition to all this, salaries fell in purchasing power the day after they were collected.

In Konin, and probably in Warsaw, there were still no radios. We learned the news by word of mouth or by telephone from Warsaw or Łódź. The Warsaw papers reached Konin only after two days. I remember that once during an evening party a policeman in navy blue uniform came to our school and ordered us to leave. When I asked him why he told me unwillingly that the president had been murdered. That was how I learned of the assassination of Gabriel Narutowicz.

Ambition did not allow me either to resign from my job in Konin (even though my appointment as headmaster was not confirmed) or to leave Konin after only one school year. Indeed, after that year I was accepted as headmaster, and, after various visits and after the *matura* exams[1] had been held, my appointment as headmaster was confirmed without difficulty.

The city continued to die. During the school year 1923–24 the number of pupils fell to eighty. The financial situation continued to worsen. In this second year of my stay there, a great joy for me was the presence of my sister Bronia, who took a job as a teacher at the state elementary school in Konin.

Yet our two years of work went for nothing. The war wiped out the generation we trained. Of the teachers only I remain, and of the pupils only one is still alive in Konin. She had tears in her eyes at seeing me when, after forty years, I revisited Konin.

The town lay in a picturesque spot on the left bank of the Warta.

Only a few houses were on the right bank. One of these was the two-story building in which I lived. At the time, Konin did not have a sewage system. Our outhouse was about 220 yards from the house. I still remember my visits there at night with a candle in my hand and despair in my heart.

In the spring of 1924 the Warta flooded its banks. Moving cakes of ice crashed against the bridge. Someone wearing an armband shouted insults at the Konin Jews who tried to cross over to the other side of the river. At that time I felt anti-Semitism everywhere, perhaps even where it did not exist. It turned out that the unknown person was an engineer who had been made responsible for the bridge. We began to exchange sharp words. The result: a court case against me for abuse of a civil servant while on duty. This was my only contact with Polish courts. I defended myself and prepared a moving speech. The judge was human and gave me the smallest possible sentence—only a fine.

Independently of this affair, the bridge did collapse, the water over-flowed its banks, and my house was inundated. Fortunately I lived on the first floor up, where the water did not reach. But Bronia and I were cut off from the school and our fellow teachers. For many days following this, I remember that the school janitor took me by boat straight from my door to the school.

Our school was housed in a small two-story building next to the incomplete walls of the future (as they assured me it would be) school. On the first floor was the headmaster's corner, a part of the teachers' room. How often, climbing the narrow wooden stairs to my head-master's corner, was I full of despair, doubts, and fears that I would spend the rest of my life in this or another dying town!

The school finances were controlled by the school board, composed of serious citizens of Konin twice or three times my age. I could find no common language with them. The one possible exception was Mr. Mączka, the youngest. Once, upset by the hopeless financial situation of the school and the stinginess of the board, I wanted to resign as head-master. I called a meeting of the board which took place in the school at night. The members guessed what the meeting was about, or perhaps I told them—I do not remember—but they came armed with bottles of vodka. I do not know how it happened, for I drank seldom and little, but that time I became quite drunk. I only recall one member of the board dancing with a bottle on his head, in which I joined. I vomited and returned home unsteadily, supported by two other drinkers. Bronia opened the door of the apartment and was shocked at my appearance.

I realize that a person can get drunk once. But how can anyone systematically degrade himself? For me this one time was a warning that lasted the rest of my life.

Later I tried to forget the empty years spent in Konin. But twice they were recalled to me.

The first time was ten years after I had left Konin. I was then in Cambridge where I worked with Max Born, with whom I published a joint paper in the *Proceedings* of the Royal Society.[2] Every half year the Royal Society had an evening affair to which they invited those who had published in the *Proceedings* during the last period. The guests were given champagne and an opportunity to talk with members of the Royal Society about their scientific results. For those occasions a white tie and tails were obligatory. I was much honoured by this invitation, and, since I did not have tails, I set about having them made by one of the best London tailors.

Thus, dressed in my beautiful tails, I went to the top of a London bus, delighted with my marvelous appearance and my wonderful invitation. In the almost empty bus I heard someone speaking Polish, a rather unusual event at that time. I turned around and there I saw Mr. Mączka, member of the school board in Konin. It was fairly dark and Mr. Mączka did not recognize me. I turned to him:

"Excuse me, sir, but am I in London or Konin?"

We began a pleasant conversation during which Mr. Mączka said:

"I was terribly bored in Konin. I thought I'd go crazy. I saved up and came on an excursion to London."

"And how about the school?"

"It went out of existence long ago. When you left, Mr. Headmaster (for in Polish everyone is called by a title and I remained headmaster to him), the number of students dropped again. We were only able to keep up the school for another year."

"Piccadilly Circus!" called the conductor. I had to get out, quickly taking leave of my former board-member.

The second time I was reminded of Konin was in June, 1963. Someone in that town remembered that I had been a headmaster there.

But now it was quite a different Konin. From a town of the past it had become a town of the future. It is now twice as large as when I knew it. In 1970, they explained, Konin would have fifty thousand inhabitants.

I have tried to find out what happened to my best pupils. What happened to Bułka, extremely intelligent; what happened to Lewin, the best in mathematics; what happened to Weinstein, the most promising poet? Always the same answer: murdered, murdered, murdered.

The school building, they told me, was used as headquarters for the gestapo.

My old school still exists. Its present headmaster well remembers Bronia and her demonstration lessons. But of the people I once knew no one remains except one pupil. She told me about her husband, whom the Nazis murdered, and of her graduation certificate, which was lost. Then she asked me for a statement that she had passed. I signed it as the former headmaster of the school in Konin.

Einstein

When my second academic year in Princeton ended, I wanted to remain for a third at the Institute for Advanced Study. The income from the book I had written with Einstein, *The Evolution of Physics*, made this possible. However, I received an offer from the University of Toronto which I decided to accept. Einstein also advised me to do so, though he regretted that I would leave Princeton and our co-operation would be over. Nevertheless, although our collaboration was much less intense during the twelve years I remained in Canada, it did not end.

During my first academic year in Toronto, 1938–39, I worked on the problem of generalizing the equations of motion, the same problem on which I had worked during the preceding year with Einstein. In theoretical physics, when the first breakthrough is made and the difficulties overcome, it is clear that some of the initial assumptions were unnecessary, that the mathematical structure of the theory can be stated more precisely and more generally. I tried to eliminate special assumptions concerning the coordinate system and to formulate the theory for a general coordinate system that would be much more in accord with the spirit of general relativity theory.

I sent Einstein the first sketch of my manuscript. He liked the idea but made two comments that immediately changed the appearance of the whole work. He noted not only that the equations could be formulated in such a general way but also that we could describe their solution by means of the same approximation method we had already used. Next, he proposed simplifying the whole problem, skilfully changing my argument and considering the problem from another, original point of view. I wanted to talk all this over with Einstein.

In May of 1939, after not having seen him for a year, I went again to the house on Mercer Street. Some time had to pass before I felt as much at ease in his room as I had when we worked together on the equations of motion and on *The Evolution of Physics*. We talked over the new results which we had already exchanged by letter. Einstein proposed that we publish together. We decided that I would prepare the manuscript and send it to Einstein for approval. I was happy that our cooperation had outlived geographical separation. Later Einstein told me about his latest attempts to construct a unified field theory, about his disappointments and hopes, repeating several times: "I regret very much that you are not in Princeton. We understood one another well. It was pleasant to work together!"

The visit depressed me. One reason for this was that I realized that the splendid experience of working with Einstein was nearing its end. The second reason was that we talked about political affairs and Einstein was more pessimistic than he had ever been. His pessimism rubbed off on me. Einstein believed that the future of Europe had been decided by the events in Madrid and Munich, that "fate was approaching." Never before had I realized with such clarity that the political situation was so hopeless and that chaos was so near.

I felt nostalgic. Later, when we walked together across the university grounds full of sunshine and spring flowers, everything seemed the same as during our cooperation.

In September of that year Hitler occupied Poland. During the war I worked scientifically on ballistics and radar. As far as I remember I

PLATE 11. Albert Einstein and Leopold Infeld.

did not see Einstein once during this time. We only exchanged letters occasionally. I did not know what part Einstein played in the matter of the atomic bomb. After the war we were in close contact for several reasons—some connected with our activity for peace, others with our scientific work. I should like to mention here his work for peace in America and mine in Canada. I made use of Einstein's writings, especially his clever and deep article "Only Then Shall We Be Free," which he sent me.[1] Our joint work for peace, against the blackmail of the atomic bomb, enlivened our contact by letters. Later I sent him my book *Whom the Gods Love*, without much hope that he would read it. He not only found time, but he sent me a few beautiful and flattering sentences about it.

I was afraid that our contact might become superficial since it was not based on common research. For my part, I felt for Einstein admiration, mixed with some embarrassment. I did not want to write to him too often. From time to time I also received letters from his secretary, Miss Dukas, an extremely kind woman. Whenever Einstein said something nice about me, she always wrote me about it.

I have saved many letters from Einstein in this period, and I give the most interesting excerpts here in translation from the German:

23 October 1939

I can imagine also how worried you are about your sisters in Poland. I hope that women are not so endangered in such a situation. There is nothing one can do against those gangs of scoundrels. But it seems to me that destiny is *en marche*!

6 March 1941

Our work on the equations of motion, surprisingly enough, has aroused greater interest than we had anticipated then. . . .

Our work to develop a usable field theory has not been successful. More and more I am coming to the conclusion that it is not possible to proceed further with the continuum theory since the Riemannian matrix persists in appearing in it as the only natural concept. Our efforts to generalize this concept have so far not had any success.

29 November 1945

First of all, my deepest sympathy on the terrible news you have received about your relatives. The Jewish fate has horrible aspects and it is obvious that the influence of Nazi propaganda has created for us serious dangers which will persist for a long time to come. . . .

I now believe quite confidently that I have discovered how gravity and electricity are connected: but the physical verification is far in the future.

25 December 1945

I can appreciate your grief, especially since the Germans also murdered several members of my own family.

I am shocked that, in this country, the reaction to these shameful crimes is not as strong and spontaneous as one might have expected.

I am very anxious to know more about your work and will gladly talk to you about the interesting possibility of a unified field theory when you next come to see me.

I sent the Polish ambassador a letter of recommendation about Mr. . . . , since I knew from your book that he actually deserves it.[2]

In these last letters there is a characteristic change in Einstein's attitude to one problem on which he worked for thirty-five years and on which he certainly worked to the last moments of his life. It was the problem of a unified field theory, a theory that would encompass the structure of elementary particles, a theory giving regular solutions that could represent elementary particles. He began many such attempts, and he announced with conviction that they contain part of the truth after which he had sought for his entire life. Later he saw imperfections in the new theory and subjected it to the most severe criticism. He believed that the general problem has no solution. Later he again thought that he saw a new light. Will this theory which he left as he was dying survive the crucial test of time as have the special and general relativity theories? I doubt it. But the attempts will remain a lasting monument to the endurance of the mind that persisted for thirty-five years on one problem so difficult that it exceeds human powers. Indeed, many people work on the problem of elementary particles, attacking it from quite another direction. The problem looks quite different today from what it did thirty-five years ago, thanks to the quantum theory that Einstein helped to create and that he regarded distastefully, in the last years of his life, as an ugly theory. He believed that a truly beautiful theory describing reality cannot make use of statistical methods.

I quote another letter from Einstein:

21 April 1946

I read with great pleasure your pamphlet on the atomic bomb[3] though, unfortunately, I haven't yet had time to study your last paper. Today I sent you a copy of a letter about our baby [that is, *The Evolution of Physics*] which will undoubtedly be as pleasant for you as it was for me.

Please don't be angry with me that I have written you so infrequently; the devilish passion to find a solution for these most difficult problems has held me pitilessly in its clutches and has forced me to make desperate efforts to overcome the mathematical difficulties. I am sending you a copy of my latest paper in which the general method of solving the problem is correctly set forth, but in which the field equations were not yet completely solved. The final draft of the paper has been at the printers now for many months. I shall send a copy to you as soon as it is available. I believe that, at long last, I have caught at least a glimpse of the truth.[4]

In the last years of his life—indeed from the time he began to work on a unified field theory—Einstein was scientifically isolated. Many physicists, myself included, did not believe that his was the proper approach to the fundamental problems of science. I remember still earlier, when I came to Princeton in 1936, Einstein had proposed that I work on one of two subjects. The first was the problem of motion, the second a unified field theory. Without hesitation I chose the first, and later Banesh Hoffmann joined us. The young physicist Peter Bergmann undertook the second subject and for a time worked on it with Einstein. (In 1949, after I had cooperated with Einstein for thirteen years on the problem of motion, about which I shall write presently, I thought that this problem was completely solved. But even today, a quarter of a century later, I am still pursuing it with my assistants.) I was quite upset that Einstein was so isolated and that he was rather outside the mainstream of physics. Often this great physicist said to me in Princeton: "Physicists regard me as an old fool, but I'm convinced that the future development of physics will go in a different direction than heretofore." Today Einstein's objections to quantum mechanics have not lost any of their force. I believe that nowadays his views would be less isolated than in 1936.

Yet, at the time, I believed that Einstein's distaste for quantum theory was unfounded. (It is true that none of this distaste was reflected in *The Evolution of Physics* since we did not want to make it a polemical book.) This is also the reason why, when one of the founders of quantum theory—Professor X—was in Toronto on the way to Princeton, I requested him to discuss the bases of this theory with Einstein. In 1937 the great Niels Bohr had been in Princeton and, during a public discussion, had tried without success to convince Einstein to accept the structure of modern quantum mechanics. I wrote to Einstein that Professor X (I do not wish to give his name here) would be coming, and I asked Einstein to receive this physicist and discuss these problems with him. I also wrote how much I admired Professor X.

In reply I received a letter containing the following comments:

20 September 1949

I, too, have the highest regard for Professor X. His scientific imagination deserves the greatest admiration, and he is always very critical of his own thoughts. But it is very difficult for me to have a debate with him because many arguments under discussion have completely different weights in his eyes than in my own. He does not appreciate my strict adherence to logical simplicity and my lack of confidence in the merit of ever impressive confirmations of theories, whenever questions of principle are involved. He considers such an attitude odd and unrealistic as do all those who firmly believe that quantum theory has come very close to reality. I understand this very well and I do not make any effort to create confusion in anybody's mind. If no one forces me to (like the various authors in the Schilpp volume which is about to be published), I am satisfied to live in my isolation and to struggle in silence with my problems.[5]

A few words about Einstein's last comment. Schilpp's book, to which he referred in the letter, was a large collective volume which was part of the "Library of Living Philosophers," edited by Paul A. Schilpp. It consisted of contributions in part intended to be critical. Included were articles by Niels Bohr and Wolfgang Pauli. In general, the publishers had planned that Einstein write about himself, his life and work, and at the end answer the critiques given by other contributors.

I know the history of this volume since I also wrote for it and was in touch with the publishers. At the end of the book appears Einstein's beautifully written reply to the objections raised in the other essays. This statement, perhaps better and more clearly than his other articles, expresses Einstein's attitude to quantum theory.

One day in 1948 I received a letter from Einstein concerning the problem of motion, with which I had not been dealing for a long time because of my war work. In this letter Einstein quoted the objections of the mathematician [Norman] Levinson to our approach. Levinson observed that there was no proof in our paper that the approximation method could be extended indefinitely, that each step could be followed by a next. We had taken only two steps—the first Newtonian and the second, the [relativistic] one that followed it. As a basis of comparison I might say that if the first step is as difficult as swimming the English Channel then the second is as difficult as swimming the Atlantic Ocean. We took that second step; the third would be as difficult, in comparison, as interplanetary travel. Thus, it did not seem to me possible that anyone would ever want to take the third step. In fact, my student and I later proved that it will never become necessary to take it.[6] However, I did not know this in 1948, and the mathematician Levinson wanted exactitude. He wanted a proof that every following step is possible if the preceding one has been made.[7]

Einstein wrote me a lengthy letter on this subject, stating that we must complete our work by sketching such a proof, and he proposed that we should publish it together. (In the end his proof was shown to be false.) This letter once again started our intensive work on the problem of motion. This time it progressed by means of a very active correspondence. I have a whole folder of Einstein's letters, unfortunately soaked during an accident to the ship that brought my things from Canada to Poland. The letters are scarcely readable where the sea water mingled with the ink.

In the beginning of this work Einstein was the enthusiast. Later it turned out that there were many other unanswered questions connected with the problem of motion, and we obtained extensive results that either deepened our previous concepts or represented completely new ones. It was now eleven years since the beginning of our cooperation—a long time and enough that we could look upon the old results from a new perspective. At this time I was developing my own school in Canada and had a very able young Ph.D. with whom I published a number of papers and with whom I could discuss all these problems.[8]

I exchanged letters with Einstein two or three times a week. Yet the basic difficulty remained: how were we to set up our approximation method in a proper mathematical form? Once, on the way home from the university, I suddenly had an idea—to introduce gravitational dipoles. Their existence ought to enable a solution at every approximation. Then, since they have no physical meaning, we must eliminate them after completing the approximation process. From the conditions at the time when the dipoles vanished we would then obtain the equations of motion.

I arrived home feeling very excited. I wanted to make the calculations at once and find out whether the idea would work. After fifteen minutes I saw that this was a simple solution to the difficulty which had held us up for a long time. After dinner I went back to the department in order to discuss this solution with the young colleague I just mentioned. I was amazed that this bright and clever young man had great difficulty in understanding the idea which seemed obvious to me. This was another proof of something I had long observed: if someone thinks of something himself he loses perspective and imagines that everything is clear, even banal; but for someone else who is sceptical of the method, difficulties appear—sometimes new and sometimes those that have already been seen, quickly solved, and forgotten by the originator.

My colleague promised to check the whole calculation. Next day he said that he had found a mistake. I did not believe him and it turned out that I was right. It was he who had made a mistake and not I. That same day I wrote to Einstein informing him briefly of my method and saying that it eliminated all the difficulties. I waited impatiently for his answer. It came, but it disappointed me enormously— it contained not a word of praise for my method. Indeed, it still dealt with Einstein's own approach to the difficulties he was trying to remove by a method different from mine. I found a mistake in Einstein's reasoning and wrote him about it, asking him to please read again the letter in which I believed I had given a solution for our difficulty. His answer began with the following words:

22 November 1948

You are quite right with your objections to my remarks about the divergence of the approximating equations. I write you only today because I had still hoped to find the letter in which you had offered some proof for your theories. But I was not successful. I had not read your letter with sufficient care because I had no doubts about the justification of my own thoughts which were based on breaking down the Bianchi identity. And so I should like to ask you to send me a copy of your remarks.⁹

It seemed to me that our cooperation required that we meet. I wrote to Einstein that I would come to Princeton. I telephoned his home from New York only to find that he was in a hospital in that same city and wanted me to get in touch with him immediately. My call was answered by a doctor who told me Professor Einstein wanted me to come as soon as possible. As far as I remember, Einstein was then in a small, private hospital housed in a two- or three-story building. On my arrival I had to wait while he was given a treatment. Finally I saw Einstein in an old, worn robe. He looked much worse than he had nine years earlier (we had not seen each other since 1939). I asked him what was the matter. He answered, laughing aloud, "That the doctors don't yet know. They'll find out at the autopsy."

We went upstairs to a sitting room and, as always, we began at once to talk about our work together.

I knew Einstein well and I knew that it did not do to interrupt him. He talked about the trouble he still had with his work. Apparently he had completely forgotten my letter. When he finished, I asked him to let me explain how I believed I had overcome the difficulty. I got out only two sentences—about the fact that it is necessary to add the gravitational dipoles, that they guarantee the integrability of the equations and that the later removal of the dipoles gives the equations of motion. As always when he was thinking, he began to stroke his moustache and then ask questions. I knew that this was his method, that he did not like lectures, only discussion. When I had answered three questions Einstein exclaimed enthusiastically, "Well, then, our problems are solved. Why didn't you write me about it?"

In relation to the last question I maintained a diplomatic silence. Then we began to talk about other things. I thanked him for the few extremely flattering sentences he had written about my book, *Whom the Gods Love,* without my requesting him to do so. He replied that the book had indeed appealed to him. And then he added with a somewhat spiteful smile, "I know you; you really wrote about yourself!"

Of course in this case he was quite wrong, unless the comment had some hidden meaning which I did not understand. In the evening we ate supper together with the doctor who was his host, and his family. We agreed that I would return next day. I was afraid that he would find some new difficulties. Nothing of the sort. He only asked me one more question in order to be sure that everything really came out all right in the calculations (he himself never checked them). Then we talked about how to formulate the paper. We agreed that I would send him the manuscript and then incorporate all his suggestions.

I am afraid that these few pages may give the reader the impression that I solved all the greatest difficulties. This was not the case. I have written about only one difficulty I did solve. The rest, as we had decided, we arranged by correspondence. Here are a few excerpts from Einstein's letters to me after our meeting in New York:

6 December 1948

We agree on one thing: the problem is basically solved, and the question that remains is how best to present it. The pedagogical side is really important in this case, because, otherwise, nobody would understand it and some other people would unnecessarily spend time in trying to solve the problem. Even if it takes some time, we must try to present our solution in the best possible way.

6 April 1949

I gladly accept the draft as edited by you. You have done a very good job. But it is still not too easy for the reader since we have still not quite succeeded in presenting the fundamental principles involved, at least as far as our basic ideas are concerned.

But I agree that everything should be published in its present form (after careful examination).[10]

Still earlier he had written me a letter which ended with the following words: "The work we have done together has given me enormous pleasure. I believe that neither of us could have done it alone because the matter is very treacherous."[11] In this way our third important work was done. It later appeared in the *Canadian Journal of Mathematics*.[12]

At about this time I received an invitation to visit Poland and, when it was known that I was to go to Europe, an invitation to Dublin came from my former department head Professor Synge, and a little later from England, from Birmingham and Manchester. Obviously, I chose to lecture on my work with Einstein, which was then at the printers and of which I had the first proofs. I wrote to Einstein that I was going and asked if he agreed to my making some small corrections in his own work which he had sent me as an editor of the *Canadian Journal of Mathematics*. I also asked if he agreed to my lecturing in Europe on our joint work. I received an answer which included the words:

20 March 1949

Thank you for your letter of 16 March. It is perfectly all right with me that you make small changes in my manuscript. Neither do I have any objections if you should want to present our work in lectures in Poland or in Dublin. I should, of course, be very glad if we could see each other before your departure so I could learn what you have in mind. I appreciate it that you did not send me birthday greetings. It was, anyway, as if I had attended my own funeral.[13]

I returned to Canada from Poland with the proposal that I spend a year there with my family. After what I had seen in Poland, the proposition appealed to me. But I very much wanted to obtain Einstein's opinion. After I returned to Canada I wrote him a short letter to which he replied:

Saturday, 11 June 1949

I am very glad that you are back again and hope that you have not become too deeply involved in world affairs. People are like shifting sands and one can never be sure how things will be tomorrow. We both have certainly enough experiences in that respect. In any case I am very anxious to get to know something about your general impressions in Poland.[14]

Part of the summer holidays after my return from Poland I spent with my whole family in New Jersey. From there, in June of 1949, I went to visit Einstein at Princeton. I must have felt that this was the last time I would see him since I was anxious for my family to meet him—that is, my wife, my son who was then ten, and my six-year-old daughter. Since I expected to have the usual long talk with Einstein, we decided that I would first go in alone, the family to join me after an hour. Somehow I remember but little from that visit. Yet I do remember that I asked Einstein his reaction to my going to Poland. He thought a moment and then said: "No one can have anything against it. It's very generous of you, but . . . ."

I waited for him to continue. And then he said something which surprised me very much but did not disturb me. "What will happen to you if the old regime returns to power? What will happen if the Soviet Union agrees to that in the final peace treaty?" I tried to explain to Einstein that such an eventuality seemed to me so unlikely that I regarded it as impossible. I do not know whether he believed me.

Not long after we had returned to Toronto I received a letter, again on scientific matters, which ended as follows:

20 June 1949

I have often wondered whether, out of idealism, you might not get too deeply involved with the Polish problem. In spite of great sympathy with the present government in Poland I cannot help being very doubtful about the stability of conditions there. After some time the evil men may emerge from the mouse-holes in which they are now hiding—not much different from what happened in Germany in the twenties. These people will then make life very difficult for you. Even if conditions in the West are most disturbing today it is not to be assumed that the present hysteria will continue for a long time or even develop into an intolerable situation. People are too well off: they are not likely to go to extremes as long as they have enough to eat.[15]

It is good to know that there were some things about which Einstein was not right. I mean about the United States and Poland. However, these words moved me because I knew how little he was concerned with individual human affairs and how much he was concerned with the laws of nature. And his words were apparently dictated by a concern for my fate.

At this time we again began to work together scientifically. Einstein wrote me a letter in which he gave an idea for simplifying the equations of motion:

16 December 1949

. . . I believe that we still have not solved our problem completely, but are hiding behind some formalism. The solution which we published is correct but we both no doubt feel that the dipole method represents an avoidable roundabout way.[16]

Einstein wanted to change the theory in such a way as to obtain the solution of the equations of motion without the dipoles. We began an exchange of letters. When it appeared that we had come to agreement on all details, again a difference appeared between us. I had already sent Einstein the finished manuscript of our joint paper when we once more failed to understand one another. I felt that we had to meet personally to discuss the new work, which still lies in my files. Unfortunately something intervened making it impossible for me to see Einstein. Our last work together will never see the light of day.

I quote part of another letter from the period of which I write:

Saturday, 23 December 1949

Please don't believe that, due to negligence, I have not yet stated my views about your proposals. I have pondered over them again and again until I reached the conclusion that they do not represent a correct solution. I worked so hard over the problem that I almost went out of my mind. I started six letters to you, but each time I had to discard what I had thought was the solution of our problem. But now I believe to be on the right track—unless the devil has again fooled me.[17]

Once more I could not agree with Einstein's solution and we put off the whole matter to our next meeting which, unfortunately, never took place.

I went to a meeting of mathematicians and theoretical physicists in Vancouver, in which P. A. M. Dirac and H. Bhabha participated. Then I returned to Toronto and put in my request for a leave of absence so that I could spend a year in Poland. The dean assured me that neither he nor the president had anything against my going.

The weekly *Ensign*, a Catholic publication sold mainly in front of churches in Montreal, gave over one whole number to my intended visit to Poland. It said that I was an atomic scientist, that I had learned atomic secrets from Einstein, and that I was going to take them behind the iron curtain. Suddenly all hell broke loose around me. How I felt, what I went through under the pressure of an increasing blackmail intended to keep me from going to Poland, does not belong to this chapter. I write about it here only because when this sheet appeared and George Drew, leader of the Opposition, asked in Parliament what the government was doing to prevent me from going, I knew that the road to the United States was closed to me and I would never again see Einstein. Hordes of journalists telephoned, pestering both Einstein and me, asking whether it was true that I had the secret of the atomic bomb. (The idiocy of all this is the more obvious since, at the time, the Soviet Union had already carried out its first atomic test explosion.)

Nearly a year after my last visit to Einstein I travelled to my native land. In Poland I received a very moving letter which I put away so carefully that I cannot find it. In it Einstein wrote about how sad he felt after the death of Ehrenfest (a well-known Dutch physicist) and after my leaving the American continent.[18] He also answered the letters I wrote him on many matters. But this was no longer the full, hand-written correspondence I had received from him before. I regret now how casually I treated these letters. Many I gave to colleagues and friends. Some I lost, not realizing what value they would some day have for me when their author would no longer be among the living. I answered in handwriting, not keeping a copy, and often I do not know to what Einstein's answers refer.

After I was in Poland I received a letter with the following postscript:

13 October 1950

In earlier times, man was merely a football in the hands of blind force—today, he is, in addition, a football in the hands of bureaucrats. But man has accepted that. Do you know that remark by Lichtenberg: "Man learns little by experience for every new stupidity appears to him in a new light"?[19]

A month later he wrote to me on scientific subjects connected with my work in Poland. The following question apparently gives his answer to my comments on my work for peace:

13 November 1950

You do know how deeply I am longing for real peace. I believe that in the present misguided situation, direct methods, that might be used for the purpose, can hardly be successful since each side has no confidence in the honesty of the other. I myself do not know of any direct suggestions to make. At present, it is possible only to consider partial steps which the individual states might take and which might be capable of slowly rebuilding the confidence which is indispensable for bringing about supranational security.[20]

I had never had a signed photograph of Einstein, and while I was in America I never wanted one. I began to regret it when I was in Poland. When I asked him for one, I received the following answer:

28 November 1952

I am glad to send you the photograph you asked for; I only hope that the winds that are now blowing may not force you to hide it at some time.

You also asked me about some scientific problem, I assume about the field theory. At present I have nothing that I have recently published on that subject. However, the inherent difficulties and alternatives have been entirely removed. . . . However, the possibility of verifying the theory with realistic conditions is unfortunately still far away.[21]

Two years later:

8 December 1954

I was happy with the good news about your life and your work. I share your optimistic feeling about the present international situation: one could hardly have hoped for such a favourable change.[22]

In 1955 I attended the celebration of fifty years of relativity theory. I received two invitations—one to Berne and the other to Berlin. In Berne there was (in July) a scientific session connected with this anniversary while in Berlin there were two lectures, on the eighteenth and nineteenth of March. The first, on March eighteenth, was given by Max Born in West Berlin, on the occasion of the fiftieth anniversary of quantum theory; I gave the second, on the nineteenth in East Berlin, on fifty years of relativity theory. I thought I might meet Einstein in one of the two cities. I wrote to ask him to come to Berlin. Though I knew there was not much chance that Einstein would come to Europe, I wanted to do as the organizing committee asked—for both East and West Berlin. The letter I received in reply was written months before Einstein's death:

17 January 1955

I am unfortunately (or should I say, fortunately) not well enough to attend such official gatherings. I believe it would be most desirable if you should explain in your lecture that the centre of the theory lies in the *general* relativity principle. For most of today's physicists have not yet comprehended this.[23]

How I fulfilled my task the reader may judge since my Berlin lecture was published in *Naturwissenschaften* (1955).[24] I only know that so many listeners turned up it was necessary to move from the academic hall to the largest in the university, and it was completely filled. The lecture was attended by physicists from the Federal Republic of Germany and a delegation from the German Democratic Republic.

On 18 April 1955 Einstein died. The great light went out. Probably the greatest physicist of all times had died, a man of unprecedented goodness—a goodness stemming rather from the intellect than from the heart. There died a man who was the conscience of the world, who always raised his voice in defence of the oppressed, always against tyranny. For me, the writing down of these memories, the rereading of the letters in that small, even handwriting was a solace for the loneliness I felt. I do not know whether they can give anyone even a weak impression of the greatness, the true greatness with which I had the good fortune to be in contact.

Niels Bohr and Einstein

I saw Niels Bohr for the first time in February of 1937 at Princeton. He came for a few days' visit and was received like a ruling monarch. I had long wanted to hear him and meet him. Like Einstein, he was almost a legendary figure for physicists. Whoever had been to Copenhagen spoke in glowing terms of the scientific atmosphere there and of the exceptional kindness Bohr showed to everyone. I had often tried to fulfil my wish, but had always encountered bad luck. Bohr was in Cambridge before me and not long after me. I had planned to attend one of the yearly meetings of theoretical physicists which he organized in Copenhagen during vacations, but Bohr became ill and the meeting was called off. During my short visit to Copenhagen I did not find him there. It was necessary to cross the Atlantic and go to Princeton in order to see and listen to Niels Bohr of Copenhagen.

Bohr, Einstein, and perhaps Planck, were the greatest names in the older generation of physicists who had the strongest influence on physics in the first half of our century. Today all three are no longer among the living and have passed into the history of science. I shall not try to answer the question: was Einstein or Bohr the greater? This evaluation should be left to the next generation. I shall only state that they represented entirely different types of mind. In order to make this difference more precise, I shall use a certain comparison from the history of science. I should add that I take full responsibility for this comparison which is entirely my own and not the official voice of science. But it is a fact that many physicists with whom I have discussed this subject have agreed with me.

From the history of science the mind closest to Bohr's seems to me that of [Michael] Faraday. Since a hundred years lie between these two men, it is not possible to push the analogy too far. Nevertheless, the similarity undoubtedly exists, and it is possible to cite characteristics common to these two thinkers. Both exhibited striking originality in scientific thought. Faraday formulated new concepts in the theory of electricity, entirely different from those of his predecessors. He had the brilliant intuition necessary to break with the concepts of classical mechanics in describing phenomena in this branch of science. Exceptional simplicity and originality—these were the qualities of Faraday's thought. The same was true of Bohr. He understood that we cannot use the concepts of classical mechanics to describe the inner structure of the atom. It was he who first used quantum theory to describe the atom, just as it was Faraday who first used the concept of a field to describe the phenomena of electricity and magnetism. After both those discoveries came an unprecedented development of new branches of physics.

But the analogy can be carried further. Both were capable of vision going beyond the existing limitations. Faraday saw the lines of force in the electric and magnetic fields where his contemporaries saw only empty space, free from all physical problems. It was only necessary to hear Bohr once, to watch the motion of his hands, the pictures and models he showed, in order to realize that Bohr really visualized how the atom is constructed, that he thought in pictures which he had constantly before his eyes. Still another analogy: both used comparatively simple mathematical methods. Of course, the hundred years of physical development separating the work of Faraday and Bohr make it impossible to take the analogy too literally. Faraday did not possess profound mathematical tools. In relation to the refinement in modern theory coming from the achievements of mathematics, Bohr's mathematics is extremely simple. Bohr's strength lies not in mathematical analysis but in the great originality of his imagination, his ability to see concretely, in pictures, and to discover new relations not anticipated by anyone else.

Einstein represents an entirely different type of mind. If we are to make a comparison from the history of science, in his case it would be with Newton. Einstein thought in logical categories and made much less use of pictures than did Bohr. The general law of gravity, first formulated by Newton, was the result of fifteen years of mental effort and remained the final, basic solution of this problem for more than two centuries—until Einstein formulated the general relativity theory. This theory, which attacks the problem of gravitation for the first time since Newton, is the result of ten years of mental effort by its creator. Once formulated, it provided the basic solution of the problem and the work of others did not contribute anything that would change the essentials of the theory.

The question, who was the greater—Newton or Faraday—is meaningless even from the perspective of the present day. All the more naive and meaningless would it be to catalogue and enumerate people like Einstein and Bohr.

Einstein's and Bohr's views on the physics of their time (1937) were entirely different. Bohr saw the progress of quantum physics during the last few years as an essential achievement which would remain in future science. Einstein was sceptical. He opposed the use of statistical methods and believed that the present state of physics was temporary. In this view of the state of contemporary science, Einstein was completely isolated in 1937, and he knew it. He understood the enthusiasm of the young resulting from the tempo of their work, from the fact that the frontiers of knowledge were being pushed forward so rapidly. But no one could convince Einstein of the latest achievements in the new physics.

Einstein's name is generally associated with the theory of relativity. But he made a basic contribution to another field of science—the application of quantum theory to the phenomenon of radiation. His work played a fundamental role in the development of this theory. His decisive step consisted in the introduction of statistical method into science—the very thing he opposed. When I asked Einstein at the time why he opposed this method, which he himself had introduced, he answered, "I introduced it as a provisional means, as a temporary necessity, but I didn't imagine that others would turn that necessity into a virtue."

In the twenties, the *Physical Review* carried a paper by Einstein and his coworkers outlining these views.[1] Not long afterward the same journal published Bohr's work attempting to answer Einstein's objections to the then current physics of the atom's interior.[2] One of Bohr's coworkers told me how often Bohr had changed the formulation of this work, constantly weakening its polemic tone, saying that a lack of courtesy in discussion is always evidence of a lack of understanding the opponent's argument.

As far as my own conviction is concerned, I must admit that, while I was in Princeton, I was more influenced by Bohr than by Einstein on the foundations of quantum mechanics, despite the fact that Einstein often tried to explain to me his way of thinking. Now, eight years after Einstein's death, I believe that he was probably right. But the basic problems of quantum mechanics are extremely complicated. Modern physics is difficult, yet anyone who comes to know it deeply loves it and will always be a physicist rather than be concerned with its foundations. At the same time, these problems are inaccessible to the philosopher.

But to return to 1937 in Princeton. The directors of the Institute for Advanced Study organized something in rather bad taste—a fairly public discussion between Einstein and Bohr. I was present, together with other curious onlookers. Apparently the chief purpose of Bohr's visit to Princeton had been to convince Einstein of the method of quantum physics.

Only now do I understand how unpleasant this meeting must have been for Einstein. He was a lonely sort and he did not enjoy contact with people; although he tried to hide it as well as he could, such meetings never pleased him. Bohr, on the contrary, was extremely gregarious—lectures and discussions with people gave him great pleasure.

PLATE 12. Peter G. Bergmann, Albert Einstein, and Leopold Infeld.

Einstein hardly ever appeared in his dark suit—a very old one, the only one he possessed—he wore it with a collar such as nowadays goes with tails, and he wore a long black tie. I remember that to the discussion he came dressed up in his festive attire. But he said very little—only a few words. Bohr interrupted him with arguments, having the support of the audience. It was like a soccer match between Poland and West Germany, held in Warsaw. The final result of the discussion was such as might have been anticipated—both Bohr and Einstein stuck to their previous views.

Besides this meeting, Bohr gave two lectures in Princeton in 1937. It is hard to imagine a worse lecturer. He spoke so softly that he could hardly be heard even in the first rows. For the packed hall where he lectured, it was necessary to use a loudspeaker. Since he had a blackboard and moved about, the microphone was attached to his lapel. He constantly got caught in the wires and had to be extracted every few minutes. He supported himself on the table with one hand, which he constantly rubbed with the sponge in his other hand; he talked as though to himself. The individual words were each expelled separately, not smoothly joined in sentences, and he continually interrupted his lecture with self-criticisms and apologies for being unable to express himself in a clear enough manner. All this made his hour-and-a-half lecture the more difficult, since each step in his reasoning process was necessary for understanding the next one. And yet, in spite of the bad technical aspects, Bohr's lecture made an extremely deep impression. It was evident how painfully each sentence was uttered, how difficult was the exact formulation of such complicated questions. The lecturer presented deep, original ideas on the foundations of modern science. In many places Bohr directed the lecture exclusively to Einstein and frequently referred to their private talks on these problems. After the first lecture and the discussion following it, Bohr and Einstein, surrounded by a crowd of listeners, continued the argument. Einstein mainly listened and Bohr discoursed so long and vehemently that he was late for a party in his honour.

In the discussion there was first talk of the influence the new physics must have on the school curriculum. Bohr said this was only a question of time and that "It won't be possible for long to hide from the young the discoveries of the new physics. Then its influence will alter the whole method of thinking of the new generation."

From time to time during the discussion he made interesting asides. When he was discussing a mistaken paper by one of the best-known physicists, he softened his criticism with the comment that, nevertheless, this scientist was one of the best experts in the field, "because an expert is one who learns through his own experience how painful and deep are the errors one can make even in the most limited field of research."

As is usual on such occasions, at the end Bohr was warmly thanked, and praised to the skies for his contribution to science. Embarrassed, Bohr replied with an anecdote. Once upon a time at the court of a Shah there was a Persian physician. He was paid handsomely by the Shah so long as his advice brought results. When, in his old age, illness began to attack the Shah from all sides, and the physician could no longer cure him, the ruler turned to him with the complaint: "I kept you in riches for years and you can't even cure me." To this the doctor answered: "Monarch, you paid me for my knowledge; but if you were to pay me for what I don't know, then all the riches of Persia would not suffice."

This was my one and only contact with "the spirit of Copenhagen," a term known wherever physics is taught because the Copenhagen school of theoretical physics under Bohr became famous throughout the world. His school exerted a great influence on modern physics; practically all contemporary physicists have been in Copenhagen. Bohr was as well known and as respected there as the king. Today, too, although Niels Bohr is no longer alive, Copenhagen is a Mecca of physicists. His son [Aage Bohr], also a professor of physics, is a worthy successor to the father.

Professor Tamm of the Soviet Union told me the following story. When Bohr visited Moscow, Lev Landau, also a Nobel prize winner, asked him, "How is it that Copenhagen is such a famous centre of theoretical physics and trains such brilliant people?"

Bohr answered: "Truly, I don't know. Perhaps only because we are not afraid to ask silly questions in order to clear up what we don't understand."

Oppenheimer

When I went on leave in the year 1965–66 I originally planned to spend five months and ten days in the United States and twenty days in Copenhagen. I wanted at last to spend a little time in that strongest European centre of theoretical physics. To use a modern phrase, I could say that I fulfilled my plan 100 percent. It would be an exaggeration, but one could probably get away with it in offices for controlling plan fulfilment. And how was it really?

Before my trip I had corresponded with two professors at Copenhagen. One was my former student and friend, Professor Alfred Schild of Austin, who was spending the year in Copenhagen. The second was a Pole by birth, Stefan Rozental, my friend of many years, now a professor in Copenhagen. And both of them, Alfred (with his wife) and Stefan, were waiting for me at the airport. I knew from our former correspondence that most of the professors were outside Copenhagen; taking advantage of the Easter holidays they had gone to warm southern Europe. Stefan was to leave in two days and of our friends and acquaintances there remained Alfred, Aage Bohr and Dr. Koba.[1] The last named is a Japanese physicist who is very good, generally esteemed, and who left his own country to seek his fortune elsewhere. He had spent a few years in Warsaw at our Institute. Unfortunately, mainly because of my poor health, we had not given him as much time as we would have liked. He was a professor at the Institute, lectured there in English and had his research students. When he was invited to Copenhagen, he chose to leave Warsaw. He has the subtlety of people from the East who bring or send presents and then thank you many times for the mere shadow of help. They must look on Europeans as barbarians. In Warsaw I was always afraid that I might offend him, and so our conversations dealt only superficially with the topics we discussed.

He invited us to a Japanese dinner. There were many tasty dishes made by his Japanese wife, and these must have taken many days to prepare. His wife spoke only Japanese, and when I thanked her she smiled charmingly. But she did not eat with us.

To the dinner they also invited Professor Peters whom I had long wanted to meet. He had lost his position in America as a "premature anti-fascist." His former teacher, Robert Oppenheimer, testified against him, and, as a result, it became impossible for Peters to support himself in America. He had gone to India where he had worked with Professor Bhabha.[2]

Here I must interrupt this flow of memories. I have mentioned Professor Koba as a physicist close to me who was in Copenhagen. I mentioned the dinner at which I met Peters, Oppenheimer's former student. These memories take me to Bhabha who has nothing to do with this story. But too many recollections press on my pen for me to ignore them. Allow me then to devote a parenthetical recollection to Bhabha.

I first met him in Vancouver in 1949, at a theoretical physics course where he and Dirac were the brightest stars. He was the greatest physicist of India, so handsome and with such a fine figure that women were mad about him. I myself saw how a beautiful Canadian model lost her mind at his appearance. He had the hauteur and pride of someone chosen by fate, which had not denied him fortune, position, intelligence. But at the same time he was wise enough to keep a tight rein on his pride. I saw him many times afterward. In 1955, at the height of his fame, he chaired the first international atomic energy conference in Geneva where American scientists and those of our countries met together. It was the first breaking of the ice, and, in this, Homi Bhabha played an honourable role. I also heard his beautiful speech that opened the conference.

Later he came several times to Poland. As the delegate of India to the International Atomic Energy Agency in Vienna he often saw W[ilhelm] Billig, Polish plenipotentiary in charge of the peaceful uses of atomic energy. The development of relations between two such opposite types of people as Bhabha and Billig interested me very much. Billig is quiet, modest, says little. Bhabha is sure of himself, proud, impressive. And yet (as Bhabha admitted to me) something of a friendship developed between them.

When we three went to the palace in Nieborów for dinner, Bhabha, looking at the rooms on the first floor up, turned to me and said: " You have a very attractive summer residence here." I had to disillusion him by saying that I was not a maharajah in Poland, and that it was not my residence.

Bhabha had studied at Cambridge and had written many papers which will long belong to the literature of theoretical physics. But in recent years he had also undertaken administrative duties so that, as he told me himself, he could only do research during his vacations.

The last time I saw him was at a Pugwash Conference in India. Nehru was to have been at the farewell banquet, but just then he had his first attack. In his place came his daughter, Indira Ghandi, now premier. Bhabha presented me to her and was charming to me, inviting me warmly to come to Bombay as his guest. On the photograph I received from this occasion we three appear together.

This story about Bhabha, which has led me to Vancouver, then to Geneva, Vienna, Poland, India, I must end with a painful memory from Dallas.[3] Every day at about six o'clock the paper boy threw the paper with a bang at our door. One day, I turned the pages quickly and there, on one of them, I discovered that an Indian jet had crashed on Mt. Blanc. All the passengers were lost. One of them was Homi Bhabha, India's delegate on his way to a conference in Vienna. This news threw the world of physicists into mourning.

PLATE 13. Indira Gandhi and Leopold Infeld 1963.

Homi Bhabha was a Parsee. They are a small but extremely influential sect in India, composed mostly of great industrialists in
Bombay. They are followers of Zoroaster. After death their bodies
are exposed on a high tower where vultures tear off the flesh and the

clean bones fall to earth. The parsees have forbidden flight over these towers. They fear the meeting by which the insubstantial spirits might float away with the material airplanes.

Basically, it is immaterial to those who die whether they are eaten by worms in the earth or vultures in the air. Each one of us must some day die. (I'm ashamed of the banality of that sentence.) But each of us expects to die in bed. It must be terrible if death suddenly hits one full force in one's car as it did Dr. Harris,[4] or in a plane as with Homi Bhabha, at the very moment when he was on a trip dictated by social duty.

So ends this sad story, which I felt I had to insert into my memories when they touched on India's greatest contemporary theoretical physicist, Homi Bhabha.

Let us return to Copenhagen, to Professor Koba's home and to my conversation with Peters. We spoke much about Oppenheimer. His personality has interested me for over thirty years, since I first met his brother in Cambridge. Later, in Princeton, in Toronto, in Copenhagen, and in Warsaw, I met a number of his former students, friends, and enemies. Once in Washington I met Oppenheimer himself. For the end of the story connected with his name we must move once more to Dallas, in 1965. And so I shall begin a section that I should entitle: The Robert Oppenheimer Affair as Seen through the Subjective Glass of Leopold Infeld.

In Dallas, Ivor Robinson gave me a book by Haakon Chevalier entitled *Oppenheimer: The Story of a Friendship.*[5] I took in the book at one gulp, not because it dealt with people I had known at various times in my life, but because it is very well written and the strange story of the friendship is told with restraint and a certain frankness. Before I return to the book, I must say a few words about my relations with people treated by the author.

In Cambridge, as I have already recalled, I met Frank Oppenheimer, younger brother of the then already well-known physicist Robert. Frank, if I recall rightly, had finished his doctorate; he came to see me several times in my modest bachelor apartment. I believed that he was either a communist or near to it, as were nearly all young people I knew well at the time. I remember that he incessantly smoked Gauloises cigarettes and urged me to smoke them too, and I now consider them the best.

In Cambridge, Frank's brother Robert was then held to be an able person who published rather too much; it was said that some of his papers had mistakes in them.

Not many years later fate took me to Princeton. There I met Robert's students and in particular one of his women students with whom I became friends, a friendship which outlasted my stay in Princeton. And so I heard a great deal about "Opie," as he was generally called by his students. He was their idol, particularly the idol of the communist students, of whom there were many in the 1930s. They were under the influence of the master, imitated his way of walking, his quiet convincing voice, his bent head, his unkempt hair.

Once when I was talking with my friend about European physicists and the fact that America lacked a name like Dirac, she said "Oppenheimer is the equal of Dirac." This comparison seemed to me so ridiculous that I abandoned the discussion.

When, in 1945, Truman announced the explosion of the first atomic bomb on Hiroshima, the whole world learned that the father of the bomb was Opie who, with a whole pleiad of physicists, had worked at Los Alamos. (It is interesting that no one knows the name of the Soviet or French physicists who are connected with independent discoveries of the bomb but everyone knows Oppenheimer's.)

My friend, who admired Oppenheimer tremendously during her studies in California, did not have bitter enough words to describe his behaviour and character after 1945.

It was 1947 or 1948. I was a professor in Toronto. Unexpectedly I received a telegram signed by Professor [George] Gamow inviting me to Washington for a round-table discussion on subjects connected with the theory of relativity, astrophysics, and quantum mechanics. I had known that such discussions took place in Washington every year and were attended by Nobel prize winners and the best-known physicists. Why I suddenly had that honour I do not know. My wife claimed it was because the year before I had attended, for the first time, a big meeting in Washington, and my report had made a good impression. Perhaps. Among those present were [Julian] Schwinger, [Richard] Feynman, my friend from Princeton H[ugh] P[ercy] Robertson, Edward Teller, and also Robert Oppenheimer.

There was something fascinating about Oppenheimer's silhouette. Some people have the power to fascinate. Robert Oppenheimer was

PLATE 14. Tenth Washington Conference on Theoretical Physics, 1947.

Back row, left to right: S. Forbush, W. Whitehead, N. P. Heydenburg, U. Fano, D. Inglis, P. Abelson, G. Gamow, M. Tuve, M. Osborne, R. Roberts, R. Alpher, B. van Evera.

Front row, left to right: H. Weyl, E. Teller, M. Schwarzschild, C. Critchfield, J. Wheeler, R. Feynman, R. Oppenheimer, J. Schwinger, G. Breit, H. Babcock, H. P. Robertson, L. Infeld.

undoubtedly one of them. Slim, almost ethereal, seemingly carelessly dressed, but behind that façade one suspected that he thought about every detail, from a fanciful hat to his tie. One immediately felt in him what the English call "leadership." He himself did not speak, gave no report, but revealed the greatest and widest erudition, classified everything and everyone.

Now, after many years, when I recall those few days spent in Washington, some of Oppenheimer's interjections seem to me to have been tactless and not well thought out. In order not to speak only in unsubstantiated generalities, I will give two examples. During the discussion, Oppenheimer said that Einstein had formulated the equations of motion from the field equations. I consider it untactful that he did not turn to me or to any of the other people I have named, although he well knew that I had been coauthor of that paper.

The second example: Schwinger presented for the first time his theory of relativistic renormalization for which he received the Nobel prize in 1965. Everyone there was enthusiastic. Oppenheimer said "All our troubles are taken care of for the next fifty years." I consider that sentence superficial and unwise. True, the work by Schwinger and Feynman took care of many difficulties, but it uncovered deeper ones. No one has ever yet solved all theoretical difficulties for the next fifty years.

Yet I must admit that there was generally much culture in Oppenheimer's remarks, which gained particularly by contrast with the comments of Teller, which sometimes bordered on vulgarity.

One evening during my stay in Washington, I sat with Robertson in the large lobby of the Park Hotel where the conference members stayed. Oppenheimer joined us and I must admit that he was charming. We talked of literature, of the latest books, which he knew and read, and on which he had definite opinions.

I saw him for the last time in a Washington restaurant, in the company of generals to whom he was explaining, no doubt, the arcana of strategy.

When I was in Berne in 1955 for a conference on the fiftieth anniversary of the theory of relativity, I talked about him with Professor Pauli. Pauli told me that Oppenheimer was trying to return to physics, but without success. In fact, if I am not wrong, no paper by him on physics has appeared since the war. That means that for more than twenty years he has ceased to be a physicist.

However, he did give popular lectures that appeared in print. I tried to read some of them but they were too clever for me. Words, words, words, but in combinations I did not understand. Once I talked about these articles with a well-known physicist, a Nobel prize winner. I admitted that I did not understand them. And he said, "I don't understand them either, and Dirac told me he didn't."

One of my closest coworkers and friends, Alfred (because of whom I went to Copenhagen), spent a year in Princeton after the war. He told me that before one entered Oppenheimer's room one passed through another room in which was a closet containing state documents so secret that a sergeant constantly guarded them and telephoned every half hour to Washington to report that everything was all right and that no one had broken in and that no one had stolen anything.

In 1954 the Oppenheimer affair broke out again. It was during Eisenhower's administration. A specially appointed commission began to dig into his past to find out whether he was a loyal citizen, whether he had ever cooperated with communists, whether he had not lied to his superior generals and colonels. The sympathy of almost all physicists was on Oppenheimer's side, especially as he was a victim of McCarthyism and had opposed the making of the hydrogen bomb, which Teller supported. Physicists divided into two groups: most were on Oppenheimer's side; only a few followed Teller. The majority of the commission examining the affair voted that Oppenheimer was not worthy of having state secrets. How to take from him those he already knew, that the commission did not say.[6]

The introduction was necessary to show clearly that, in the difference of opinion between Oppenheimer and Teller, my sympathy was with Oppenheimer. But is Oppenheimer without sin?

A few years ago I met Haakon Chevalier in Poland. His name was closely connected with the Oppenheimer affair. He came to see me and told me in detail how he had suffered as a result of the fantastic inventions of his friend. When we tried to understand what could have made Oppenheimer betray his friend to the extent that the friend lost his university post and had to leave the United States, Chevalier could find no answer. He told me that he had written a book called *The Man Who Would Be God*, in the form of fiction, in which he analysed his relation to Oppenheimer. In his latest book, which in contrast to the first was written as autobiography, he explained the genesis of the earlier title:

> When I was in New York—this was in March 1948—I ran into Philip Morrison, who had been, before the war, one of Opje's firmest friends and who had worked closely with him. . . .
>
> After we had discussed a variety of things and reminisced about a number of friends, I began to wonder why he hadn't yet mentioned Opje. . . . At last I could no longer restrain my curiosity.
>
> "What about Opje?" I asked.
>
> Phil did not answer at once. He looked unhappy. He made a vague gesture with his hands.
>
> "I hardly see him any more," he said at last.
>
> He explained, rather reluctantly, that he found it hard now to communicate with him. "We no longer speak the same language. . . . He moves in a different circle. . . ." He told how, one of the last times he had seen Opje, he had been kept up in the air for a long time by Opje's periodic references to "George." As Opje kept saying, "George thinks this . . ." and "George says that . . . ," Phil finally asked him who "George" was.
>
> "You understand," Phil explained to me, "General Marshall to me is General Marshall, or the Secretary of State—not George. This is typical. . . ."
>
> He went on to say that Opje had profoundly changed. And then, unexpectedly, I heard him say,
>
> "He thinks he's God."[7]

This conversation suggested to Haakon the title of his novel, which appeared in 1959. Haakon sent me a copy. To tell the truth, I found it disappointing. The subject did not lend itself to fictional treatment, the people were wooden and the psychology incomprehensible. The reviewer for *Czytelnik* Publishers had the same opinion; he said that the book was not worth translating.

At last Haakon decided to write down the whole story as it really occurred. The result of this decision is quite a fascinating book.

When I met Haakon in Warsaw, he was about sixty. In his youth he must have been unusually handsome. Strongly built, he was a type that is very attractive to girls. He was a mixture of French, Scandinavian, and American. He seemed to me to be straightforward, intelligent, but not over-refined.

The rest of what I shall write is based on Haakon's book, about which I wrote in the introduction. This is how he wrote about it:

He and Opie were professors at the same university, and gradually their acquaintance developed into a great friendship. It was based on their common radical social outlook, which was not limited to talk but showed in work for trade unions and support for the Spanish cause. Haakon came to admire Opie, even though his creative ability did not equal his highly refined manner of thinking. There was a whole galaxy of physicists contemporary with Opie who were much better than he, but he was able, after a few weeks in Holland, to give a lecture in Dutch (unnecessarily, since his audience understood English), and he was the only physicist who knew Sanskrit. Externally, as well, it is difficult to imagine greater contrast than between Haakon and Opie. The former had an athletic build, the latter was weak and slim and looked as though the slightest breeze would blow him away.

The tragedy began from a very small incident. In 1943 an engineer named [George C.] Eltenton talked with Haakon about the necessity for cooperation between Soviet and American scientists, for exchange of information of strategic importance for the good of the common fight against fascism. Eltenton suggested that Opie, known for his left-wing outlook, might help in this matter. Haakon writes in his book that he refused to be a go-between and so disliked the implications of this conversation that he thought Opie should know of it in order to be on his guard. During a party, when they were alone in the kitchen together to prepare drinks, Haakon told Opie about the conversation. That is Haakon's version, in which the reader may believe or disbelieve as he chooses.

The affair seemed so unimportant to Haakon that he soon forgot it. Of course, there is no proof whether Haakon told the whole truth when he recalled this incident, though the book makes the impression of being sincere.

The next part of the story took place in 1946 at an FBI office in San Francisco where, after interrogating Haakan for nine hours, the agent informed him:

"I have depositions from three scientists who worked on the atomic bomb. Each of them states that you approached him three times trying to get secret information about the atomic bomb in the name of Russian agents."

Oppenheimer

The tragedy approached farce. Which three scientists? He was supposed to have approached each of them three times, or nine in all. The
FBI agent did not want to give their names. Where did this strange,
improbable accusation come from—something from Kafka's world?

From that time on, an FBI sedan constantly followed him. Every
step was followed.

The next episode was a meeting with Opie and the first shadow on
their friendship. Oppenheimer stated that since their last meeting his
views had moved considerably to the right, that he did not like either
the Soviets or the American Communist Party. Haakon still looked
on him as a friend, however, and told him about his experience and
interrogation by the FBI. To this Oppenheimer proposed that they go
out into the garden, no doubt because he was afraid of eavesdropping
in the room. Haakon asked him about the origin of the supposed triple
effort to obtain secrets. Opie didn't answer this and only became
extremely nervous. When his wife asked them to return to the house,
since the guests were waiting, he burst out with a flow of vulgar words.

During the next few years repercussion of the FBI interrogations
increased. Haakon lost his job and his wife, and all doors were closed
to him. But he still believed in Oppenheimer's friendship and continued
to see and visit him. He was refused a passport to visit France. But, since
he had dual citizenship, he decided to go on a French passport.

The correspondence between Haakon and Oppenheimer continued.
In 1953 they met for the last time at supper in Paris. There was a
strained atmosphere between them and they avoided political subjects.
Haakon arranged a meeting between Malraux and Oppenheimer.
There Opie spoke an untrue sentence to the effect that it was very
sad for those close to Einstein and for those who had respect for his
earlier work, but they must admit that during the last twenty-five years
Einstein had done nothing in science.

That this was untrue will be clear later. But here the question is
pertinent: what had Opie done in science for the last twenty years?

Let us return to the story of Oppenheimer according to Haakon's
book. From 12 April to 6 May 1954, Opie was formally interrogated
in Washington by a special commission in the presence of the prosecutor
and his two defence counsels. During these interrogations Haakon
continued to believe in the innocence and good will of Opie. The
storm broke on 16 June of that year when the transcript of the hearing

was published in about a thousand pages. The world press immediately excerpted the most juicy parts, playwrights began to write dramas on the subject, using the transcript for the scenario. No doubt in the future Hollywood will add its two cents. Haakon quoted many pages of the transcript, especially the part that dealt with "the Chevalier affair." I do not know, and I do not think anyone knows, the real truth of the affair. I shall deal only with facts revealed by the transcript.[8]

The affair broke out in 1954, but its beginning went back to 1943. Witnesses appeared in this order: Lieutenant [Lyall] Johnson, Colonel [Boris T.] Pash, and Colonel [John R.] Landsdale. Opie had told Johnson that someone he knew but did not want to name had approached three physicists at Los Alamos with the proposal that they betray secrets of the atomic bomb to the Soviets. This information was sent up to increasingly higher echelons. At last, pressed to tell who was the go-between, he mentioned Haakon Chevalier. Finally Haakon knew that Opie was the source of his difficulties and persecution.

How can one explain all the lies? From the transcript it emerges that Oppenheimer had no scruples about naming as communists his brother Frank as well as many of his former friends and associates. (I learned from Peters that Opie, in the transcript, accused him of escaping from a concentration camp by "subterfuge." Was there a legal way? We know what it meant for people to be thus branded in the United States at that time.)

He made a deposition in 1954 that the 1943 affair concerning the three scientists supposedly asked to betray secrets was made out of thin air. When asked, "Why did you do it?" he answered, "Because I was a fool."

The history of the 1950s knows many cases of overzealous people who scented betrayal where there was none. But to invent a story that threatened a friend and not tell him anything about it for eleven years while maintaining friendly relations with him, and then explain it by saying, "Because I was a fool"—this is the only such case known to me in the history of science.

Most upsetting is the style of the interrogation. I read in *Dialog* a translation of the play by Heinar Kipphardt that was based entirely on the transcript of the interrogation.[9] But the author had to condense 992 pages into one script. Thus, everyone speaks in well-rounded sentences, and the figure of Oppenheimer emerges as a hero except for the sentence, "Because I was a fool," which the author could hardly omit. But in the transcript the triviality of Oppenheimer's testimony and the words of the interrogators are amazing. No one would imagine, on the basis of these depositions, that Oppenheimer was the intelligent, highly refined scientist who knew Sanskrit.

But enough of Haakon's book. Let us move on to the epilogue of the affair. Let us return for a bit to Dallas. It was the middle of December, warm, and I was sitting with my wife at the Center, in that large, well air-conditioned office. I was sitting at the desk and doing calculations. In the next room Gwen was typing on her electric machine. Across the desk sat Helen reading the New York *Times*, which came to the Center every day by airmail. It was because of the New York *Times* and my subscription to *Newsweek* that I knew what was going on in the world and, thanks to *Życie Warszawy* [*Warsaw Life*], what happened in Poland ten days before. My wife interrupted my calculations: "This article is very interesting." I quote it here in its entirety:

OPPENHEIMER'S VIEW OF EINSTEIN WARM
BUT CRITICAL

by Henry Kamm
Special to the *New York Times*

Paris, Dec. 13—A warm and admiring but not uncritical portrait of Albert Einstein was drawn tonight by J. Robert Oppenheimer.

1. Einstein commanded the love of everyone, the American physicist told an audience of about 1,000. But he added that long before his death, Einstein lost touch with the profession of physics.

2. "Things had been learned, but they had come too late in his life," he said.

3. Dr. Oppenheimer, director of the Institute for Advanced Study in Princeton, devoted his address to the last years of Einstein's life, when, he said, "we were close colleagues and something of friends."

4. The physicist spoke at the opening session of an international symposium marking the 10th anniversary of Einstein's death and the 50th of his General Theory of Relativity.

5. The three-day symposium is sponsored by the United Nations Educational, Scientific and Cultural Organization at its headquarters.

6. "Einstein's early work was paralyzingly beautiful," Dr. Oppenheimer said, "but full of errors."

7. "Correcting the errors had delayed the publication of Einstein's
collected works for 10 years," Dr. Oppenheimer said. He added:

8. "A man whose errors take 10 years to correct is quite a man."

9. He portrayed Einstein as a lonely man amid universal admiration
and as a scientist who had been bypassed by the science in which he
was a giant.

10. "In the scientific community," Dr. Oppenheimer said, "Einstein
founded no 'school' and did not have many students as apprentices
or disciples." Those who worked with him, he noted, were
significantly called "assistants."

11. Dr. Oppenheimer said the common assumption that Einstein
played a vital role in the development of the atomic bomb, with
which he himself was closely connected, was "not, in my opinion,
true."

12. Even the letter to President Roosevelt early in the war in which
Einstein and other scientists sought to make the President aware of
the military potential of splitting the atom, was not important, he
said.

13. "The letter had practically no effect whatever," he declared.[10]

I have added numbers before the paragraphs in order to refer to them
more easily later. But, before that, a few details about which it is not
easy for me, even today, to speak calmly. At first I thought that the
whole world would read the article and one should therefore protest.
I thought that I should not do it since I was only a temporary guest
in America. When my anger subsided I wrote to my friend Peter
Bergmann in New York, one of the best relativists in the world and a
former assistant of Einstein. The good Gwen typed the letter and I
sent six copies to my associates, including Einstein's secretary, Helen
Dukas, and Professor [André Léon] Lichnerowicz.

This is the letter I sent them:

15 December 1965

Dear Peter,

I was quite shocked by the article entitled "Oppenheimer's View of
Einstein Warm but Critical" on page 39 of the *New York Times* for
December 14. I am very much disturbed about it and I believe someone
ought to write a letter to the *Times*. I thought about doing it myself

but I don't believe it would be quite fitting. However, if you wish, I will sign such a letter with you and perhaps others, if you would prepare the outline.

I am looking forward very much to seeing you in Dallas.

With warmest regards,

Leopold Infeld

Bergmann answered that in the New York edition the article had been hidden on page 88, that he would not have read it if not for my letter, and that an answer would only draw attention to it. Miss Dukas wrote that Einstein, were he alive, would not want anyone to answer if someone spread nonsense about him. It is true that he never paid the least attention to what was written about him. Besides, Miss Dukas wrote me that we must wait for the opinion of Otto Nathan, who was the lawyer in charge of Einstein's estate and who had been his friend. He was then in Paris and, after his return, would give his opinion.

Lichnerowicz agreed with me. He had been at the lecture and wrote to me, " I protested! "

Professor [Andrzej Mariusz] Trautman of Warsaw, who was taking my place at the Institute, was also to have been in Paris but arrived a day late because he did not get his passport on time, and thus he had not heard Oppenheimer's lecture.

Later I received further news on this affair straight from Bergmann and Helen Dukas. Oppenheimer had asked Miss Dukas and Einstein's daughter to go with him to Paris to hear the lecture! Later he claimed that he had been misquoted. But Otto Nathan informed Miss Dukas that the lecture was worse than the summary in the *Times*. I have read the lecture and it seems to me that the summary in the paper gives an objective sample.[11] Miss Dukas wrote to me again—a bitter letter concerning this incident. But there has not been any answer to the criticism of Einstein. I am sorry that I must do it myself. I would like the Polish reader at least to know what I think of those criticisms.

I shall begin with a question addressed to UNESCO. Why should that famous and valued organization have chosen Oppenheimer as its principal opening speaker without consultation with the world of physicists? Even before the war Oppenheimer had written only one paper dealing with relativity theory and that one was coauthored with someone else.[12] The paper is still sometimes quoted today. But a whole group of people worked with Einstein, wrote papers or books in this field, and are widely known both as scientists and excellent lecturers. I am not thinking here of myself, since the time when I was able to lecture is past.

And now we come to the essence of my objections in the hope that I do not speak only in my own name.

1. The first sentence is generally correct. One comment need be added: "Einstein lost touch with the profession of physics." He was never a professional physicist, and that genre of people, spread over America, among the lesser physicists, was alien to him throughout his life.

2. The second sentence requires broader explanation. Einstein is one of the creators of quantum mechanics. He turned away from its development with distaste during the years of his maturity and old age. Once when I asked him, "Why don't you like the statistical methods in quantum mechanics which you yourself introduced?" Einstein answered, "I introduced them as something temporary but I will never agree that God plays dice."

Was Einstein right? Like most physicists, I rather think not.

By the 1930s Einstein already expressed little interest in quantum mechanics. Modern physics is for the young with very elastic brains who can keep up with the quick changes in theory. One or two years is the average life of such theories. Einstein was never interested in this type of physics. He built or wanted to build ironclad theories that would last for years. Such were his special and general relativity theories which today, eleven years after Einstein's death, are more alive than in 1955. Unfortunately, this fate is not shared by his unified field theory that, nevertheless, is still the source of inspiration for many mathematicians.

6. His works were "full of errors." To what errors does Oppenheimer refer? Neither I nor any other physicist with whom I have spoken understands that sentence.

The work of every physicist can be divided into stages. At every stage he thinks he has completed his work on that lode of gold which he has uncovered. Then it turns out that it is only the surface vein of a much greater lode and that he must search deeper. From this point of view the work of every physicist is a step-by-step search for the truth.

Newton's laws are the truth today, too, but only for small velocities. A fool might say that Newton's work was full of errors since it does not apply to high speeds approaching that of light.

I know of no errors by Einstein aside from the usual printing errors and those that Einstein knew well, since they drew him, in his subsequent work, closer to the truth.

7. Professor [Valentine] Bargmann (not to be confused with Bergmann) has been in charge of the publishing of Einstein's work for ten years. He is a professor at Princeton University, a splendid mathematician and physicist, a man of great culture, whom I know well from the time I spent at the Institute in Princeton. He is now in poor health and has many duties; Einstein's works are mainly written in German and their publication does indeed take long. Then, if Bargmann had said that the reason for the ten-year delay is mistakes in Einstein's works, I would be surprised but would believe it. But I do not believe Oppenheimer.

10. "Einstein founded no 'school'. . . . Those who worked with him . . . were called 'assistants'." It is true that Einstein prepared only occasional lectures, never gave systematic courses and did not conduct seminars. But his school was the whole world of physicists. His works resulted in a flood of papers in the most distant corners of the earth.

Einstein usually had one assistant who helped him in making calculations. During my time in Princeton, this assistant was Peter Bergmann. When he left and then worked, as he still does, as a well-known scientist, his place was taken by E[rnest] G[abor] Straus.

But did he not have collaborators? There is a large book known to every physicist called *Albert Einstein, Philosopher-Scientist*. This book was published by P. A. Schilpp in the "Library of Living Philosophers." It appeared in 1949, the year when Einstein was seventy. At the end of the book is a bibliography of all Einstein's works. Let us look, for example, at the ten years 1935–45. In 1935 there appeared Einstein's famous critique of quantum mechanics, written together with his assistant N. Rosen and B. Podolsky, an independent scientific worker who had never been Einstein's assistant. Today, that work lives and is vividly discussed.[13]

In 1938, the book I wrote with Einstein appeared and was translated into all the languages of the cultural world.[14] The author of these words does not think and has never thought of himself as

Einstein's "assistant." In that same year appeared the paper on the problem of motion in relativity theory—neither Hoffmann nor I were ever Einstein's "assistants."[15] As for me, I was no longer even a fellowship-holder at the Institute in Princeton, and Hoffmann was a professor in New York. In 1940, there appeared a new work by Einstein and me that developed by correspondence between Princeton and Toronto, where I was on the staff.[16]

In 1941 a work of Einstein's with Bargmann and Bergmann appeared.[17] By then they were both well-known serious scientists and to call them "assistants" would be grotesque.

In 1942 a paper appeared by Einstein and the Nobel prize winner Wolfgang Pauli. To call him an "assistant" would seem to be an exaggeration.[18]

Again, in 1944, another of his papers, this time with V. Bargmann appeared. Bargmann was then a professor at Princeton.[19]

In 1945 Einstein was sixty-six, pension age, when one cannot expect to have the high flow of imagination that a young physicist has. Oppenheimer came to know Einstein when the latter was already retired. This he does not mention at all. I remember Einstein in his forties during a seminar in Berlin when his intellect and his deep understanding shone forth. But he continued to work and have new ideas to the last day of his life. How important some of these papers were can be indicated by the following example. When Einstein was seventy, we wrote a long paper together, mostly by correspondence. I will not be so modest as to say that all the ideas in the paper came from the brain of Einstein, but I will be sufficiently objective to admit openly that the majority of those ideas were Einstein's.[20] After Einstein's death, I continued to work on the same problem and, with a docent at my Institute, wrote a book on the subject. Its main source is precisely the paper I had written with the seventy-year-old Einstein. The list of various papers on this subject given in that book (written by myself and Jerzy Plebański, and published in 1960) covers five closely printed pages, and it is certainly not complete.[21] So much reaction resulted from the paper by Einstein in his seventieth year, coauthored with someone who was not an "assistant."

11, 12, and 13 refer to the atomic bomb and Einstein's part in this undertaking. Probably, if Einstein were alive, he would be glad of what Oppenheimer said. But was it the truth? I do not know but very much doubt it. From Einstein's secretary I learned that, long before the war (even before I went to Princeton), Einstein was invited by Roosevelt to the White House for several days and nights, that he slept in Lincoln's bed and had long and secret conversations with the President the contents of which he never revealed. I cannot imagine that Roosevelt did not feel Einstein's charm and did not notice his simple and superhumanly deep wisdom.

And there is another argument. The letter to the President is dated 1 August 1939. This was during the period when the military subsidies for the atomic bomb increased.

Moreover, such a statement, which disagrees with that of historians, requires some sort of proof. How did Oppenheimer know of this? From the President? In general it would not be worth while to argue about this whole thing. Whether or not Einstein's letter had an influence is immaterial. But it is not immaterial that two American bombs destroyed two Japanese cities. And here another picture related to Oppenheimer's person comes to mind.

We returned from a dinner with friends to our apartment in Lazy Acres, Dallas. My wife looked at the television program and saw that on Channel 13 (the one without ads) there was an hour devoted to the history of the atomic bomb. We quickly turned on the TV but were only in time for the end of the program, when various people connected with the production of the atomic bomb were asked whether they thought that the decision to drop the bomb on two Japanese cities was correct.

I recall that the decision was President Truman's and was contrary to the position of scientists who advised that it be dropped on a Japanese wilderness. They understood that Japan, having good physicists, would realize the destructive force of the American bomb and would sue for peace, and, thus, the massacre of innocents would be avoided. But no! As we know, the military won. Now, after twenty years, the question was put again. We heard only some of the answers, by people who did not interest us much. But then Teller appeared on the TV screen. With amazement I heard him say that today he thought that to drop those atomic bombs on cities had been wrong.

My wife and I heard this sentence with our own ears. Then Oppenheimer appeared. The last time I had seen him was thirty years previously.

How people change! Grey haired, one-dimensional, he spoke in a weak voice, saying that dropping the atomic bomb on the two Japanese cities had been the proper step.

Now let us return to Copenhagen, to the dinner, to Peters and our conversation. Peters recalled the years of his youth, the marvelous atmosphere of interest in physics that Oppenheimer created and his fascinating lectures.

"And why did he change so much?" I asked.

"Because he had a weak character," said Peters. And I think that in that simple answer lies the key to understanding his behaviour. Einstein often said: "Scientific work is mainly a matter of character." And as always, he was right about this, too.

Oppenheimer died while I was writing this book.

Despite the saying that one should speak only good of the dead, I decided to write these words about his life because I do not believe that sayings contain the wisdom of man, in particular when they refer to a figure that belongs to history.

The
Centenary
of
Max Planck

Modern physics, that is of the twentieth century, is characterized by two constants: the speed of light, represented by the letter c, and Planck's constant, represented by the letter h. Both these constants appear in the theory of relativity (especially c) and in quantum theory (mainly h).

The constant h was first introduced in 1900 by Max Planck to explain difficulties in the theory of radiation. He had the courage to show that we must accept a certain discontinuity, characterized by h, in order to obtain the proper formula for the radiation of a black body. That was the beginning, as yet timid and limited, of quantum theory. Later, thanks to the work of Bohr and many others, it became clearer how important h is in the description of reality.

I met Planck when I was a young student, and attended his lectures. In the autumn and winter of 1920–21, I spent one semester in Berlin where Planck was then lecturing on thermodynamics. He was already over sixty—thin, bald, pleasant and straightforward in his manner. It was, I think, the year before he retired.

I was never especially interested in thermodynamics, and Planck's lectures were a summary of his book, which I had already read. His perhaps too smooth lectures seemed to me rather boring. I remember once that Planck, who spoke without notes, became lost in the middle of a proof and could not extricate himself. He calmly took a card containing formulae from his pocket and continued with its help.

Planck's course in theoretical physics took three years. Within this time, by lecturing five hours a week, he managed to cover all of theoretical physics that was necessary for his students.

In Berlin at that time there were two chairs of theoretical physics. The more important was held by Max Planck and the other by Max von Laue (like Planck, a Nobel prize winner). Both were conservative, both hated Nazism. Planck was too old to make an active protest, but von Laue spoke openly against Nazism. I remember how Einstein told me that von Laue was the only German with whom he would shake hands. Von Laue may have been courageous, but he was a very poor lecturer. He spoke with difficulty, swallowing half his words so that one could understand him only with the greatest difficulty.

Planck himself conducted the exercises for his course—something which nowadays is done by young assistants, often not yet Ph.D.s. It is unthinkable today that a professor should do this, far less an older professor—and a Nobel prize winner. The exercises were held every Monday from nine to ten a.m. At the beginning of the hour Planck dictated the problems—usually only one of which required a real effort to solve. The solution was to be placed in the professor's mailbox exactly at nine on Thursday morning. No one dared to be late in returning his solution. On the paper each wrote his name and the number of his seat. On Monday morning when he came to his place he would find his exercise marked with the letter G (good) or N (not good). The exercise hour was spent by having someone who had given an especially good or original solution explain it at the blackboard. In order to obtain the professor's signature in his index, a student had to complete at least five problems and receive G for three of them.

Neither Planck nor von Laue created a school in the sense that Bohr, Sommerfeld, or Born did. Of course, they did create schools by the papers they wrote but not by personal influence. (So far as I know Planck had only one student who took a doctor's degree under him.)[1] Today there are many active schools of theoretical physics, including one in Warsaw. But I knew of only three centres in the twenties where such schools existed. Despite this lack, Planck's lectures were attended by about a hundred people.

In all of Germany, the dates 24–25 April 1958 marked the hundredth anniversary of Planck's birth. At that time there was no wall dividing East and West Berlin. A common celebration was organized by both parts. Afterward there was a meeting held by the East German Physical Society in Leipzig in honour of Max Planck, in which foreign guests participated. I was a delegate of the Polish Academy of Sciences.

The celebration began at one p.m.—an odd time for such an event. Half an hour earlier the Opera House, rebuilt in an exaggerated splendour, was quite full. Behind the open curtains we could see the stage covered with flowers, a bust of Planck in the centre, Planck's equations written as beautifully as a picture above the speakers' table at which sat a row of older men in black suits and wearing gold chains —the sign of the academy's honour.

A variety of speeches were given next. The president of the Berlin Academy of Sciences, Max Volmer, spoke of Planck's activity in the Academy, of his relation to Einstein and of the fact that it was due to him that Einstein moved to Berlin and became a member of the academy there. Then came a longer speech by von Laue. When I later read it in printed form, I saw that it had been a very interesting address.[2] But neither I nor any other physicist with whom I talked heard a single word. Why? There are two possible explanations. One is that von Laue spoke too softly and unclearly, and the other is that the loudspeaker was out of order just then. At the end, Otto Hahn offered the Academy the bust of Planck.

From the Opera we went to Kupferstrasse, to the Institute of Physics. This building had been given to the German Physical Society by the government of the German Democratic Republic to be used in perpetuity. The ceremony gained in importance since it was connected with the return by the Soviet Union of Planck's books, manuscripts, and notes. We looked at the exhibition and heard a fine and simple speech by the doyen of Soviet physics—Professor Abram Joffe. Lise Meitner, a former student and friend of Planck, gave a very moving talk, full of personal memories from which clearly emerged the silhouette of a fine man who, as Joffe said, belonged not only to Germany but to the whole of the civilized world.[3] The only unpleasant note in the affair was struck by the mayor of Berlin with his political jargon during the dedication of the building for the Physical Society.

At about six o'clock there was a reception at the Opera House. All the dignitaries of the German Democratic Republic attended, led by Walter Ulbricht. Because we had eaten nothing since the morning (as I said, the ceremony at the Opera House had started at one) I was terribly hungry. The food was abundant and good, interrupted only by short toasts. Professor N. Boguliubov spoke in the name of the Soviet Academy, P. A. M. Dirac in the name of the Royal Society of London, and Victor Weisskopf spoke for the United States.

In the evening there was a performance at the Opera for us but I was too tired to go.

Next day there was a ceremony in West Berlin. The two affairs were similar in that at the first, in East Berlin, von Laue of West Germany spoke and at the second, in West Berlin, one of the speakers was Gustav Hertz, the only Nobel prize winner then living in East Germany.

The meeting in West Berlin began at four o'clock in the new Congress Hall in the Tiergarten, perhaps ten minutes away from the gates separating the two zones. This new building did not resemble any other I have ever seen. Built beside a lake, it looked externally like the open jaws of a whale. To enter was no easy matter. I arrived about half an hour early and there was already a crowd gathered. The hall holds 1,700 people. But those seeking admission numbered a great deal more, mainly because Heisenberg was to speak on his nonlinear field theory of elementary particles. I met Max Born in front of the entrance and he proposed that we try to get in together. Five huskies in uniform guarded the entrance. When I showed our invitation, they said we had to enter somewhere else, down below. This meant to a nearby room in which there was only a loud speaker through which we were to hear the speech from the main hall. We obediently started toward this room, when suddenly we heard a voice saying in German: " But, Professors Born and Infeld, of course you are to go to the main hall!"

Over the protests of the guards we entered. Later the thing became clear. The guards had themselves decided to direct all those whose invitations had numbers up to 1,700 to enter the main hall; all others went to the additional room. The result was that many young students having nothing to do with physics sat in the main hall, and some well-known physicists who had come especially for the event could not get in.

The hall was strange. The walls were completely monotonous, with no paintings but only rectangular wooden slabs placed at various angles to give the best acoustics. Excellent lighting came from the ceiling. The seats were comfortable, alternately light and dark blue, like a chessboard. But in this odd hall one felt relaxed and rested. The program began with music. Then came the speech by Heisenberg with equations, drawings, and pictures projected on screens appearing where the wall opened as though by magic.

Part of the time Heisenberg talked about things I knew, and then I understood him. Or he talked of things which I did not know, and then I did not follow what he wanted to say. The lecture was supposed to be for the general public but was full of philosophical allusions which were completely unclear to me. More or less I understood this much—that he contrasted the ideas of Plato and Democritus and stated that modern physics is moving in the Platonic direction.[4] It seemed to me that the converse of his thesis would be equally true. I shall return in a moment to Heisenberg's theory, which was the main subject of the lecture. After Heisenberg, Hertz lectured—brief, witty, and with a good style—about the contribution Planck had made to experimental physics.[5]

In the same building there was a supper for some of the invited guests. I sat next to Planck's niece—an older, charming woman who told me details from Planck's life and about the death of his two sons.

PLATE 15. Leopold Infeld 1898–1968.

One was killed during the First World War at Verdun, the second was murdered by the Nazis. The unhappy Planck lived through the death of both these sons.

From Berlin we went to Leipzig by a splendid highway. And again, in front of the Institute of Physics, in Leipzig, there was a crowd of people through whom it was difficult to penetrate. Here, after the speeches of greeting, Heisenberg began the conference with his lecture, the featured point on the program. While I had been disappointed in Heisenberg's lecture during the Planck ceremony, I was much impressed by his Leipzig lecture for physicists. It had an extremely logical structure, was beautifully delivered and all important points were clearly made. I have often been asked what I think of Heisenberg's theory. I have two comments to make. First, it contains many extremely interesting ideas. Of these the most important is the introduction into Hilbert space of a metric which is not necessarily positive. As Heisenberg himself is the first to admit, this idea first occurred to Dirac long ago but its consistent use is due to Heisenberg. The second comment is that the work is still only a plan. The success of the theory will depend on its results. For these results it will be necessary to wait, and it seems to me that the creator of the theory is somewhat too optimistic about its future. In recent years the number of physicists who are sceptical about it has constantly increased.

After Heisenberg's lecture there was discussion. I was impressed by the certainty and skill with which Heisenberg answered questions and objections.

I should like to add a description of the next day, during which I had the honour to chair a meeting. Among the speakers were Bogoliubov, Soviet scientist and recently a Lenin prize winner, and Dirac, a Nobel prize winner. I, personally, was much interested in Dirac's well-formulated report which dealt with a topic from general relativity theory—a topic on which two of my students at Toronto, [Felix Arnold Edward] Pirani[9] and Schild, had worked. After dinner we had a seminar at which we discussed the report.

Some speeches were of less interest to me. One was on philosophy and full of jargon and trivialities such as we did not hear in Poland even in the worst times. But in general the Planck ceremony and the Leipzig meeting were unusually successful. They are evidence that there is a solidarity among scientists, who understand more and more clearly that science is one, and not only that coexistence is possible but, more, that cooperation—so important for the development of science— is also possible, even in Berlin.

Notes

NOTES TO INTRODUCTION (pp. 1–13)

"As I See It" was published in the *Bulletin of the Atomic Scientists* (February, 1965), 7–14.

1   Infeld, "Władysław Natanson," p. 120.

2   Infeld, *Quest: The Evolution of a Scientist* (Garden City, New York, 1941), p. 322.

3   On the development of the physics discipline see R. McCormmach, "Editor's Foreword," *Historical Studies in the Physical Sciences, 3* (1971), ix–xxiv; P. Forman, J. L. Heilbron, S. Weart, "Physics *circa* 1900. Personnel, Funding, and Productivity of the Academic Establishments," *Hist. Stud. Phys. Sci., 5* (1975), 1–185.

4   L. Pyenson and D. Skopp, "Educating Physicists in Germany *circa* 1900," *Social Studies of Science, 7* (1977), 329–66.

5   Infeld, *Quest*, p. 255.

6 Infeld, "Einstein," p. 142.

7 Infeld, *Quest*, p. 279.

8 Infeld, "Einstein," p. 141.

9 A. Einstein, "Autobiographical Notes," trans. P. A. Schilpp in Schilpp, ed., *Albert Einstein. Philosopher-Scientist, 1* (La Salle, Ill., 1949), 17.

10 Infeld, *Quest*, pp. 271–72.

11 Infeld, "Einstein," p. 146.

12 Infeld, *Quest*, p. 280.

13 *Ibid.*, p. 283.

14 *Ibid.*, p. 282.

15 *Ibid.*, p. 318.

16 Infeld, "Einstein," p. 145.

17 *Ibid.*, p. 145.

18 L. Pyenson, "Einstein's Early Scientific Collaboration," *Hist. Stud. Phys. Sci., 7* (1976), 83–123; M. J. Klein, *Paul Ehrenfest. The Making of a Theoretical Physicist* (Amsterdam, 1971).

19 See J. L. Heilbron's review of L. S. Feuer, *Einstein and the Generations of Science* (New York, 1974), in *Science, 185* (1974), 777–79.

20 Antonie Pannekoek was a distinguished Dutch astronomer and historian of astronomy. He was associated with Rosa Luxemburg's *Spartakusbund* and, as Karl Hörner, he was attacked by Lenin in *Left-Wing Communism, An Infantile Disorder*. Gerrit Mannoury was a Dutch linguist and mathematician, also a communist. Dr. Rudolf Grossmann was a philologist and a member of the Ibero-American Institute in Hamburg. Under the pseudonym Pierre Ramus he wrote many socialist-anarchist books and pamphlets during the period 1910–25.

21 Infeld, *Quest*, p. 289.

22 *Ibid.*, p. 291.

23 A. Einstein, "Autobiographical Notes," p. 17.

24 Infeld, "Oppenheimer," p. 180.

25 A. Einstein and L. Infeld, *The Evolution of Physics* (New York, 1938), p. 125.

26 Infeld, *Quest*, p. 318.

27 A. Einstein, *Lettres à Maurice Solovine* (Paris, 1956), pp. 74–75. Letter from Einstein to Solovine, 27 June 1938.

28 A. Einstein and L. Infeld, *Die Physik als Abenteuer der Erkenntnis* (Leiden, 1938). Some years later Einstein had second thoughts about the German title. He wrote to Infeld: "Das Buch sollte nicht heissen 'Physik als Abenteuer der Erkenntnis', sondern 'Die Erkenntnis mit Abenteuer'." Einstein to Infeld, 11 March 1952. Photocopy in the Einstein Archives, Princeton.

29   *Sonya Kovalevska, Her Recollections of Childhood*, trans. I. F. Hapgood, with a biography by A. C. Leffler trans. from Swedish by A. M. Clive Bayley, and a biographical note by L. Wolffsohn (New York, 1895).
30   W. H. Jordy, *Henry Adams: Scientific Historian* (New York, 1952).
31   S. Freud, "An Autobiographical Study," in J. Strachey, ed., *The Standard Edition of the Complete Psychological Works of Sigmund Freud* (London, 1950), *20*, 1–70.
32   A. Einstein, "Autobiographical Notes," p. 33.

NOTES TO "CANADA"   (pp. 17–38)

1   W. Z. Chien, V. G. Smith, and L. Infeld, "On Some Series of Bessel Functions," *Journal of Mathematics and Physics, 26* (1947), 22–28; Infeld, "The Influence of the Width of the Gap upon the Theory of Antennas," *Quarterly of Applied Mathematics, 5* (1947), 113–32; W. Z. Chien, Infeld, J. R. Pounder, A. F. Stevenson, J. L. Synge, "Contributions to the Theory of Wave Guides," *Canadian Journal of Research, A27* (1949), 69–129.
2   On the British-French-Canadian atomic energy projects at Montreal and Chalk River during the Second World War, see the official United Kingdom Atomic Energy Authority history by Margaret Gowing, *Britain and Atomic Energy, 1939–1945* (London, 1964). Other sources include Wilfrid Eggleston, *Canada's Nuclear Story* (Toronto, 1965), as well as the interview between Charles Weiner and Lew Kowarski, recorded on 19–20 October 1969 in Scarsdale, New York, and available in transcript at the Niels Bohr Library of the American Institute of Physics in New York.
3   Eric Temple Bell, *Men of Mathematics* (New York, 1937).
4   Infeld, *Whom the Gods Love* (New York, 1948).
5   "Ich bin ganz entzückt über Ihr Galois-Buch. Ein psychologisches Meisterstück, ein überzeugendes historisches Gemälde, und Liebe zu menschlicher und geistiger Grösse verbunden mit einem ungewöhnlich aufrechten Character.
      Diese Bemerkung könnten Sie, in gutes Englisch übersetzt, Ihrem Verlag zur passenden Benutzung senden. Es ist aber nicht nur so gesagt, sondern es ist aufrichtige Bewunderung dabei. Besonders wirksam finde ich die glaubhafte Zeichnung der dunklen Hintergründe dieses Dramas, überzeugend durch die Zeitlosigkeit der Situation des aussergewöhlichen Menschen. Das war wohl auch, was Sie zum Schreiben gezwungen hat; ich kann's Ihnen nachfühlen."

6   Hugh Boyd, "Atomic Uses. Forget Bombs—Infeld," Winnipeg *Free Press*, 16 May 1947, p. 3; Infeld was also quoted in a second article, "Alumni Pay Homage To Grads at Luncheon," Winnipeg *Free Press*, 17 May 1947, p. 12:

> "The level of scientific achievement is of essential importance for the strength and greatness of a country. Our best men are constantly leaving the country . . . we are exporting our brainpower and our immigration policy makes sure that we do not import it," said Dr. Infeld.
>
> "It is the competition with level of graduate work that matters most. There are much too few opportunities of research in our country. Worse than that, there is no sufficient appreciation of research in our country."

7   General Leslie Richard Groves was actually in charge of the Manhattan Project.

8   Infeld, "Atomic Energy and World Government," 18 pp., 1946, pamphlet published by the Canadian Institute of International Affairs.

9   William Lyon Mackenzie King.

10 On the defection of Igor Gouzenko and the related trial of Fred Rose, M.P. from Montreal-Cartier, see the *New York Times*, 19 February 1946, p. 1, and 19 March 1946, p. 1; Montreal *Star*, 15 March 1946.

11 Raymond Boyer, at the time Professor of Chemistry at McGill University. During the war he helped develop the explosive RDX. See the Montreal Gazette, 18 December 1948 for the outcome of the Boyer case.

12 David Shugar, employed with Research Enterprise, Ltd.

13 Edward Mazerall, radio engineer with the National Research Council of Canada.

14 Wiener comments on his life as a child prodigy in his two-volume autobiography, *Ex-Prodigy* (New York, 1953), and *I Am A Mathematician* (New York, 1956).

15 Wiener, *Cybernetics* (Boston, 1948).

16 Oskar Ryszard Lange, Polish socialist economist who taught in the United States during the Second World War. See his *Poland and the United Nations* (Detroit, 1944), as well as the "Biography of Oskar Lange," by Tadeusz Kowalik in the volume *On Political Economy and Econometrics: Essays in Honour of Oskar Lange* (Warsaw, 1964), pp. 1–13.

17 Infeld, "The Polish Question," *Canadian Forum*, 25 (1945), 10–12.

18 Probably, Jerzy Rayski and Jan Rzewuski.

Notes to pages 39–61

NOTES TO "WHY I LEFT CANADA" (pp. 39–54)

1 Halina was Infeld's second wife. See page 126.
2 Infeld, "Visit to Dublin," *Scientific American*, *181* (October, 1949),
   11–15; "Visit to England," *ibid.* (November, 1949), 40–43; "Visit to
   Poland," *ibid.* (December, 1949), 40–43.
3 In addition to Volkoff, Infeld refers to W. Opechowski (Mag. Fil.,
   Warsaw), F. A. Kaempffer (Ph.D., Göttingen), and Heinz Walter
   Koppe (Ph.D., Berlin). By 1949 many Canadians also held appointments
   in physics at the University of British Columbia.
4 Laurent Schwartz lost his position as *professeur d'analyse* at the Ecole
   polytechnique of Paris in 1960. London *Times*, 18 October 1960, p. 11;
   Le Monde, 30 September 1960, p. 6; The *New York Times*, 25 September
   1960, p. 4.
5 John Elliott Rankin, Congressman from Mississippi, a notorious racist,
   anti-Semite, and anti-communist.
6 Infeld, *Albert Einstein* (New York, 1950).
7 See Owen Lattimore, *Ordeal by Slander* (Boston, 1950).
8 William Arthur Deacon, "Exciting Fictionized Biography by Toronto
   University Professor," Toronto *Globe and Mail*, 14 February 1948;
   review of Infeld's *Whom the Gods Love*.

NOTES TO "POLAND" (pp. 55–111)

1 In Infeld's original letter, he ended this paragraph with the words, "in
   the cause of peace." A copy of the letter is with the Mathematics
   Department of the University of Toronto.
2 Infeld's letter continued with the phrase, "in my field" inserted in pen,
   and then concluded the paragraph: "and to work for peace throughout
   the world. In so doing, I am convinced that I likewise continue to serve
   the people of Canada." *Ibid.*
3 "Such action under the Canadian Citizenship Act was always legal,
   against minor children of a parent who had renounced or lost citizenship.
   But from 1914 until 1950, the child had an absolute right to reclaim
   citizenship on reaching his majority. Under the amendments of 1950,
   which Parliament approved in the days following Dr. Infeld's departure,
   the child lost this right: it was left to the Immigration Minister's
   discretion to allow an application 'under special circumstances.'" From
   an editorial entitled, "An Injustice To Be Repaired," Toronto *Globe
   and Mail*, 18 January 1968.
4 Margaret Schlauch.

5 Infeld, "Od Kopernika do Einsteina," *Kosmos*, Ser. B., *1* (1955), 209–26.
6 Einstein and Infeld, *The Evolution of Physics* (New York, 1938), p. 31.
7 Arnold Sommerfeld, "To Albert Einstein's Seventieth Birthday," in P. A. Schilpp, ed., *Albert Einstein: Philosopher-Scientist* (Evanston, Ill., 1949), pp. 99–105. Sommerfeld cites Adolf Harnack's opinion that Einstein and Max Planck are the present generation's philosophers.
8 Einstein, Infeld, and Banesh Hoffmann, "The Gravitational Equations and the Problem of Motion," *Annals of Mathematics*, *39* (1938), 65–100.
9 V. A. Fock, "Sur le mouvement des masses finie d'après la théorie de gravitation einsteinienne," *J. Physics, Acad. Sci. USSR, 1* (1939), 81–116; "On the Integrals of the Center of Gravity in the Relativistic Problem of Two Finite Masses," *Doklady, Acad. Sci. USSR, 32* (1941), 28–30.
10 A revised version of Infeld's *Nowe drogi nauki* (Warsaw, 1933) was translated by Louis Infield and published as *The World in Modern Science. Matter and Quanta* (London, 1934). Einstein wrote a short foreword for the translation.
11 See the Russian articles by Fock: "Against Unscientific Criticism of Modern Physical Theories," *Voprosy filosofi*, no. 1 (1953), 168–74; "The Concept of Uniformity, Covariance, and Relativity in the Theory of Space and Time," *Voprosy filosofi*, no. 4 (1955), 131–35; also "Das Kopernikanische und das Ptolemäische System im Lichte der allgemeinen Relativitätstheorie," *Sowjetwissenschaft* (1953), 805–9; "Die moderne Theorie von Raum und Zeit," *Sowjetwissenschaft* (1954), 525–44.
12 Infeld, "Kilka uwag o teorii względności," *Myśl Filozoficzna*, no. 1 (11) (1954), 70–79.
13 See the general discussion in Loren Graham, *Science and Philosophy in the Soviet Union* (New York, 1972).
14 L. D. Landau and E. M. Lifshitz, *Mechanics* (Moscow, 1941).
15 Rudolf Slánský (*né* Salzmann), former Secretary-General of the Czech Communist Party, executed by the Party in 1952 on charges of treason.
16 Władysław Gomułka, Vice-Premier of Poland, deprived of office in 1949; his prestige restored, he became First Secretary of the Polish United Workers Party in 1956.
17 Infeld, "Moje wspomnienia o Einsteinie," *Twórczość*, no. 9 (1955), 41–85.
18 Stalin's body was removed from the Lenin mausoleum in 1961.
19 Debate concerning relativity theory in the Soviet Union is treated in Loren Graham, *op. cit.* (note 13). See also Maxim Mikulak, *Relativity*

Theory and Soviet Communist Philosophy, 1922–1960 (diss., Columbia University, 1965).

20 L. D. Landau, "On the Quantum Theory of Fields," in W. Pauli, ed., *Niels Bohr and the Development of Modern Physics* (New York, 1955), pp. 52–69.

21 The story is attributed to other contemporary savants, notably the mathematician G. H. Hardy.

22 Kun Huang or H. W. Peng. See Max Born, *Mein Leben* (Munich, 1975), pp. 388–90.

23 Chien Wei-zang.

24 See J. Rotblat, *Scientists in the Quest for Peace. A History of The Pugwash Conferences* (Cambridge, Mass., 1972).

25 Infeld, "Kitzbühel i Wiedeń," *Kosmos*, ser. B., 5 (1959), 7–12.

26 Butlerov, Fedorov, Lebedev, and Vasilev are treated in Alexander Vucinich, *Science in Russian Culture, 1861–1917* (Stanford, Calif., 1970).

27 Infeld, "Wojna i Nauka," *Przegląd Kulturalny*, 2 October 1958.

28 Kuo Mo-zo, a founding member (1930) of the League of Leftist Writers in Shanghai. See. J. Guillermaz, trans. A. Destenay, *A History of the Chinese Communist Party, 1921–1949* (New York, 1972).

29 A notational convention proposed by Christoffel in the late nineteenth century to facilitate calculations in differential geometry. See D. J. Struik, "Elwin Bruno Christoffel," *Dictionary of Scientific Biography, 3* (New York, 1971), 263–64.

30 Infeld and Plebański, *Motion and Relativity* (London and Warsaw, 1960).

NOTES TO "WŁADYSŁAW NATANSON" (pp. 115–22)

1 Infeld probably refers to the books: M. Planck, *Einführung in die allgemeinen Mechanik* (Leipzig, 1921); Clemens Schaeffer, *Einführung in die theoretischen Physik*, 2 vols. (Berlin, 1921, 1922).

2 Arthur Stanley Eddington, *Space, Time, and Gravitation. An Outline of the General Relativity Theory* (Cambridge, 1920).

3 Natanson, "Pierwsze zasady mechaniki udulacyjnej," *Prace Mat.-Fiz.*, 37 (1930), 1–77.

4 Natanson, *Wstęp do fizyki teoretycznej*.

5 Natanson and Konstanty Zakrzewski, *Nauka fizyki*, 3 vols. (Warsaw, 1921–25).

6 Infeld notes Arnold Sommerfeld, professor of theoretical physics at the University of Munich; Niels Bohr, professor of theoretical physics at

the University of Copenhagen; Max Born, professor of theoretical physics at the University of Göttingen.

7   Born and Infeld, "Foundation of the New Field Theory," *Proceedings of the Royal Society, A 144* (1934), 425–51.

8   Natanson, "On the Statistical Theory of Radiation," *Bulletin international de l'Académie polonaise des sciences, A 134* (1911), 15 pp.; "Ueber die statistische Theorie der Strahlung," *Die physikalische Zeitschrift, 12* (1911), 659–67. See, for example, Friedrich Hund, trans. Gordon Reece, *The History of Quantum Theory* (London, 1974), pp. 29–30.

NOTES TO "KONIN"   (pp. 130–35)

1   National final examinations for secondary school students.

2   M. Born and Infeld, "Foundation of the New Field Theory," *Proceedings of the Royal Society, A 144* (1934), 425–51.

NOTES TO "EINSTEIN"   (pp. 136–52)

1   Einstein, "Only Then Shall We Find Courage," 8 pp., published by the Emergency Committee of Atomic Scientists, 1946, consisting of an interview with M. Amrine in the *New York Times Magazine*, 23 June 1946.

2   The transcribed letter of October 1939 was one of Einstein's rare English communications. The German text of the succeeding three letters follows:

6 März 1941

... Unsere Bewegungsarbeit findet merkwürdigerweise mehr Interesse als wir damals erwartet haben. ...

Unsere Bemühungen eine brauchbare Feldtheorie aufzustellen haben zu keinem Ergebnis geführt. Ich neige immer mehr zu der Ansicht, dass man mit der Theorie des Kontinuums nicht weiterkommen kann, weil in dieser sich die Riemann-Metrik fast mit Notwendigkeit als die einzig naturgemässe Begriffsbildung aufdrängt. Unsere Bemühungen um eine allgemeine Begriffsbildung hatten aber bisher keinerlei Erfolg.

29 November 1945

Vor allem mein herzlichstes Beileid zu den schrecklichen Nachrichten, die auch Sie über das Schicksal Ihrer Verwandten erhalten haben. Es ist etwas Furchtbares um das jüdische Schicksal und es ist klar, dass der Einfluss der nationalsozialistischen Propaganda noch für lange ernste Gefahren für uns in sich birgt. . . .

Ich glaube jetzt mit ziemlicher Zuversicht zu sehen wie Gravitation und Elektrizität zusammenhängen, wenn auch eine physikalische Verifikation noch in weiter Ferne liegt.

25 Dezember 1945

Ich kann Ihnen Ihren Schmerz nachfühlen, zumal auch in meiner Familie mehrere von den Deutschen umgebracht worden sind.

Ich bin recht schockiert darüber, dass die Reaktion auf diese Schandtaten in diesem Lande nicht so stark und spontan ist als man es erwarten sollte.

Ich bin recht neugierig auf Ihre Arbeit und will Ihnen gerne über diese interessante Möglichkeit einer einheitlichen Feldtheorie erzählen, wenn Sie mich einmal besuchen.

An den polnischen Botschafter habe ich empfehlende Worte für Herrn . . . geschickt: aus Ihrem Buch weiss ich ja, dass er es wirklich verdient.

3   Infeld, "Atomic Energy and World Government," 18 pp. pamphlet published by the Canadian Institute of International Affairs, 1946.

4   den 21 April 1946

Ich habe mit vieler Freude Ihre ausgezeichnete Schrift über die atomic Bomb gelesen, bin aber leider noch nicht zum Studium Ihrer letzten Abhandlung gekommen.

Heute sende ich Ihnen die Abschrift eines Briefes über unser gemeinsames Kind, der Sie sicher nicht weniger freuen wird als mich.

Seien Sie mir nicht böse, dass ich Ihnen so spärlich schreibe; der Problemteufel hält mich erbarmungslos in seiner Zange und treibt mich zu verzweifelten Anstrengungen, mathematische Schwierigkeiten zu überwinden. Ich sende Ihnen meine letzte Arbeit, in welcher der allgemeine Weg zur Lösung bereits richtig angegeben, die Feldgleichungen aber noch reformbedürftig sind. Die endgültige Arbeit ist schon seit vielen Monaten im Druck. Ich sende sie Ihnen sobald sie erschienen ist. Ich glaube endlich einen Zipfel der Wahrheit erfasst zu haben.

5   20.IX.49

Auch mir gefällt der X ausgezeichnet. Seine wissenschaftliche Phantasie ist aufs Höchste zu bewundern und er steht seinen eigenen Gedanken stets kritisch gegenüber Diskutieren aber kann ich kaum mit ihm, weil die verschiedenen Argumente in seinen Augen ein ganz verschiedenes Gewicht haben als in den meinen. Mein starres Hängen an der logischen Einfachheit und mein Misstrauen in den Wert von auch eindrucksvollen Bestätigungen von Theorien, wenn es sich um prinzipielle Fragen handelt, kann er nicht verstehen. Er empfindet solche Haltung als wirklichkeitsfremd und schrullenhaft wie alle, die fest daran glauben, dass die Quantentheorie dem Wesen der Dinge schon ganz nahe gekommen ist. Ich begreife dies sehr gut und gebe mir gar keine Mühe jemanden irre zu machen. Wenn man mich nicht dazu zwingt (wie die Autoren in dem nächstens erscheinenden Band der Schilpp-Bücher), krieche ich nicht aus meinem Mauseloch heraus sondern schlage mich still mit den Problemen herum.

6   See Infeld and J. Plebański, *Motion and Relativity* (London and Warsaw, 1960).

7   Levinson's observations were communicated orally. In the paper in which they presented their results, however, Einstein and Infeld thank, by a typographical error, "Mr. Lewison" for Levinson's insight. See, note 12, pp. 209, 211.

8   Alfred Schild.

9   22.XI.1948

Sie haben völlig recht mit dem Einwand in Bezug auf den Divergenzsatz in den Näherungsgleichungen. Ich schreibe erst jetzt, weil ich immer noch hoffte Ihren Brief mit dem bezüglichen Beweis wiederzufinden, was mir aber nicht gelang. Ich hatte den Brief nicht genau gelesen, weil ich damals an die Beweiskraft meiner auf die zerlegte Bianchi-Identität gegründeten Überlegung nicht zweifelte. So bitte ich Sie mir Ihren Beweis nochmals mitzuteilen.

10   6.XII.1948

Aber darin sind wir einig: das Problem ist im Prinzip gelöst und es handelt sich nur noch darum, wie man die Sache am besten darstellen soll. Das Pädagogische ist hier wirklich wichtig, weil sonst kein Teufel die Sache wirklich begreifen wird und immer wieder von anderer Seite an diesem Problem unnötigerweise geknabbert werden wird. Wir müssen uns einfach Zeit lassen, um diese schöne Sache optimal darzustellen.

6.IV.1949

Ich bin mit der korrigierten Fassung einverstanden. Sie haben da ein grosses Stück Arbeit geleistet. Der Leser hat es aber auch nicht leicht, weil es uns doch nicht ganz gelungen ist, das Prinzipielle vom Formalen zu trennen, wenigstens bei der Darlegung des letzten Gedankens. *Aber ich bin einverstanden, dass alles so gedruckt wird es jetzt ist* (nach sorgfältiger Durchsicht).

11 "Die gemeinsame Arbeit mit Ihnen hat mir unbeschreibliche Freude gemacht und ich glaube, dass keiner von uns allein ganz damit fertig geworden wäre. Denn der Stoff ist geradezu hinterhältig."

12 Einstein and Infeld, "On the Motion of Particles in General Relativity," *Canadian Journal of Mathematics, I* (1949), 209–41.

13 März 20, 1949

Ich danke Ihnen für Ihren Brief vom 16. März. Ich bin völlig damit einverstanden, wenn Sie in meinem Manuskript kleine Änderungen machen. Ich bin natürlich auch völlig einverstanden, wenn Sie in Polen und (oder) in Dublin über unsere Arbeit vortragen. Natürlich freue ich mich sehr, wenn ich Sie vor Ihrer Abreise sehen und das mit Ihnen besprechen kann, was Sie im Sinn haben. Auch bin ich Ihnen dankbar, dass Sie mir keinen Geburtstagsbrief geschrieben haben. Es war sowieso wie eine Beerdingung bei lebendigem Leibe.

14 Samstag 11.VI.1949

Ich freue mich, dass Sie wieder da sind und hoffe, dass sie sich nicht gar zu tief in das weltliche Geschäft eingelassen haben. Denn die Menschen sind wie Flugsand und man ist nie sicher was morgen oben liegt. Wir können ja beide ein Liedchen davon singen. Jedenfalls bin ich sehr neugierig von Ihnen etwas über Ihre allgemeinen Eindrücke zu hören.

15 20.VI.1949

Ich habe mir oft Gedanken darüber gemacht, dass Sie sich aus einer Art Idealismus zu weit mit der polnischen Angelegenheit einlassen könnten. Bei aller Sympathie mit der gegenwärtigen dortigen Regierung kann ich nicht an der Labilität der Verhältnisse zweifeln. Nach einiger Zeit mögen die Dunkelmänner wieder aus den Mauselöchern hervorkriechen, in denen sie sich jetzt verborgen halten—so ähnlich wie es in Deutschland in den zwanziger Jahren gewesen ist. Dann würden Ihnen die Brüder die Hölle heiss machen. Wenn es auch in der westlichen Sphäre gegenwärtig recht muffig ist, so ist doch nicht anzunehmen, dass der gegenwärtige hysterische Zustand gar zu lange andauert oder sich gar zu unerträglichen Zuständen auswächst. Dafür geht es den Leuten zu gut. Bei vollem Bauch werden die Leute nicht zu fanatisch.

16   16.XII.1949

Ich fühle, dass wir unser Problem immer noch nicht völlig gelöst haben, sondern uns hinter einem Formalismus verstecken. Unsere publizierte Lösung ist richtig, aber wir haben beide das Gefühl, dass die Dipole einen vermeidbaren Umweg darstellen.

17   Samstag, 23.VII.1949

Glauben Sie nur nicht ich hätte aus Nachlässigkeit zu Ihrem Vorschlage keine Stellung genommen. Ich habe studiert und studiert und wurde davon überzeugt, dass es nicht der wahre Jakob ist. Also habe ich mich das Gehirn beinahe geplazt ist. Sechs Briefe habe ich angefangen und den Weg immer wieder verworfen. Nun glaube ich den Witz gefunden zu haben—wenn mich der Teufel nicht etwa wieder an der Nase herumgeführt hat.

18   A copy of Einstein's letter to Infeld, dated 11 March 1952, is available in the Einstein Archives at Princeton. Einstein remarks, "Es dünkt mich eine Ewigkeit seit Sie weg sind. Ich fühle mich auch vereinsamt, seit der unvergessliche Felix Ehrenhaft das Zeitliche gesegnet hat. Meine einzigartige Korrespondenz mit ihm aber wird gottlob der Nachwelt erhalten bleiben." Thus, Einstein referred not to the suicide of Paul Ehrenfest (1880–1933) but, in a light-hearted way, to Ehrenhaft's (1877–1953) departure for Vienna. See Martin J. Klein, *Paul Ehrenfest. The Making of a Theoretical Physicist* (Amsterdam, 1971). A discussion of Ehrenhaft's unorthodox approach to physics, *circa* 1945, is given in Paul K. Feyerabend, *Against Method* (London, 1975), *passim*.

19   13.X.1950

Früher war der Mensch in der Hauptsache nur der Spielball blinder Kräfte—jetzt ist er noch dazu ein Spielball von Bürokraten—und findet sich damit ab. Kennen Sie Lichtenbergs Wort: "Der Mensch lernt wenig durch Erfahrung, denn jede neue Torheit erscheint ihm in neuen Lichte"?

20   13.XI.1950

... Sie wissen wie sehr mir das Streben nach einem wirklichen Frieden am Herzen liegt. Ich glaube, dass in der jetzigen verfahrenen Situation direkte Versuche der hier in Betracht kommenden Art deshalb keine Aussicht auf Erfolg haben, weil auf allen Seiten das Vertrauen in die ehrliche Absicht des anderen erschüttert ist. Direkte Vorschläge wüsste ich nicht zu machen. Einstweilen können nur Einzelschritte der beteiligten Lager in Frage kommen, die geeignet sind, langsam das Vertrauen herzustellen, ohne das konkrete Massregeln für die übernationale Sicherheit nicht zustande gebracht werden können.

21   28.XI.1952

> Die gewünschte Photographie schicke ich Ihnen gerne und hoffe nur, dass der gegenwärtig blasende Wind Sie nicht in die Notwendigkeit versetzen wird, dieselbe gelegentlich verstecken zu müssen.
>
> Sie haben mich auch wissenschaftlich etwas gefragt, wohl über die Feldtheorie. Gegenwärtig habe ich nichts Gedrucktes darüber. Es ist aber so, dass die inneren Schwierigkeiten und Alternativen völlig beseitigt sind. . . . Die Möglichkeit eines Vergleiches mit den Tatsachen leigt aber leider noch in weiter Ferne.

The date that Infeld gives is mistaken. He in fact quotes from a letter of 28 *October* 1952, omitting an earlier paragraph:

> As for these peace efforts, I am not able to take part in them; in my view they are more or less propaganda activities connected with the "cold war." Only by a genuine effort on the part of the principal nations to come to terms, and not by a lot of noisy talk in public, can there be any real hope for progress; such talk merely serves as a provocation. I am so often reminded of Heine's poem, "The Disputation," which closed with the suggestion that the rabbi and the monk both cut unpleasant figures.

Translated in O. Nathan and H. Norden, eds., *Einstein on Peace* (New York, 1960), p. 570.

22   den 8 Dezember 1954

Ich freue mich über die guten Nächrichten über Ihr Leben und Wirken. Die optimistische Auffassung über die internationale Situation teile ich und kaum konnte man eine so günstige Wendung erhoffen.

23   den 17 Januar 1955

Ich bin leider (oder soll ich sagen gottlob) nicht mehr gesund genug, um bei solchen offiziellen Anlässen zu erscheinen. Ich denke, es wäre hübsch, wenn Sie in Ihrer Predigt klarmachten, dass der Schwerpunkt der Theorie in dem *allgemeinen* Relativitäts-Prinzip liegt. Denn die meisten gegenwärtigen Physiker haben dies noch nicht erfasst.

24   Infeld, "Die Geschichte der Relativitätstheorie," *Naturwissenschaften* *42* (1955), 431–36, translated as, "The History of Relativity Theory," *Rend. Matem. e delle sue applicazioni, 13* (1955), 270–81.

NOTES TO "NIELS BOHR AND EINSTEIN" (pp. 153–59)

1   Einstein, B. Podolsky, and N. Rosen, "Can Quantum-mechanical Description of Physical Reality Be Considered Complete?" *Physical Review, 47* (1935), 777–80.

2   N. Bohr, "Can Quantum-mechanical Description of Physical Reality Be Considered Complete?" *Physical Review, 48* (1935), 696–702.

NOTES TO "OPPENHEIMER" (pp. 160–80)

1   Kobayashi Minoru.
2   On Bernard Peters and Bhabha see R. S. Anderson, *Building Scientific Institutions in India: Saha and Bhabha* [Occasional Paper Series, no. 11, Centre for Developing-Area Studies, McGill University] (Montreal, 1975), esp. pp. 37–8.
3   Infeld spent the year 1965–66 as visiting professor at the Southwest Center for Advanced Studies, an independent research institute founded in 1961 at Dallas with local university and federal funds. The Center merged with the University of Texas at Dallas in 1969. Infeld describes his experiences there in the chapter "Old Age" of *Kordian i ja* (Warsaw, 1968).
4   Arnold Harris, Infeld's doctor in Dallas, who died when his car became trapped in a flash flood.
5   Haakon Chevalier, *Oppenheimer: The Story of a Friendship* (New York, 1965).
6   See, for example, Nuel Pharr Davis, *Lawrence and Oppenheimer* (New York, 1968).
7   Chevalier, *Oppenheimer*, pp. 79–80.
8   U.S. Atomic Energy Commission, *In the Matter of J. Robert Oppenheimer. Transcript of Hearings, May 27, 1954 through June 29, 1954* (U.S. Government Printing office, 1954). The hearings were adapted by, for example, Joseph Boskin and Fred Krinsky, *The Oppenheimer Affair. A Political Play in Three Acts* (Beverly Hills, Calif., 1968).
9   Heinar Kipphardt, *In der Sache J. Robert Oppenheimer; ein szenischer Bericht* (Frankfurt a. M., 1964); translated as: *In the Matter of J. Robert*

Oppenheimer (New York, 1968). See H. Kipphardt, "Przesłuchanie J. R. Oppenheimer," *Dialog* (Warsaw), *10* (1965), no. 6, 32–91, and the discussion of Kipphardt's play in *Dialog*, *9* (1964), no. 12, 137–42.

10 *New York Times*, 14 December 1965, p. 88 of the Late City Edition.

11 Oppenheimer's address is published as "Einstein's Presence" in *Science and Synthesis. An International Colloquium Organized by UNESCO on the Tenth Anniversary of the Death of Albert Einstein and Teilhard de Chardin* (Berlin, 1971), pp. 8–12.

12 J. R. Oppenheimer and G. M. Volkoff, "On Massive Neutron Cores," *Physical Review*, *55* (1939), 374–81, connected with the preceding article by R. C. Tolman, "Static Solutions of Einstein's Field Equations for Spheres of Fluid," *ibid.*, 364–73.

13 Einstein, Boris Podolsky, and Nathan Rosen, "Can Quantum-mechanical Description of Physical Reality Be Considered Complete?" *Physical Review*, *47* (1935), 777–80.

14 Einstein and Infeld, *The Evolution of Physics* (New York, 1938).

15 Einstein, Infeld, and Banesh Hoffmann, "The Gravitational Equations and the Problem of Motion," *Annals of Mathematics*, *39* (1938), 65–100.

16 Einstein and Infeld, "Gravitational Equations and the Problem of Motion II," *Annals of Mathematics*, *41* (1940), 455–64.

17 Einstein, V. Bargmann, and P. G. Bergmann, "Five-dimensional Representation of Gravitation and Electricity," in the *Theodore von Kármán Anniversary Volume* (Pasadena, Calif., 1941), pp. 212–25.

18 Einstein and Pauli, "Non-existence of Regular Stationary Solutions of Relativistic Field Equations," *Annals of Mathematics*, *44* (1943), 131–37.

19 Einstein and V. Bargmann, "Bivector Fields, I," *Annals of Mathematics*, *45* (1944), 15–23.

20 Einstein and Infeld, "On the Motion of Particles in General Relativity," *Canadian Journal of Mathematics*, *1* (1949), 209–41.

21 Infeld and Jerzy Plebański, *Motion and Relativity* (London and Warsaw, 1960).

NOTES TO "THE CENTENARY OF MAX PLANCK" (pp. 181–87)

1 Planck's students before the First World War included Max von Laue, Moritz Schlick, Kurt von Mosengeil, Ernst Lamla, Walter Schottky, Erich Henschke, and Arthur Coym.

2   M. von Laue, "Zu Max Plancks 100. Geburtstag. Vortrag vor der Deutsche Akademie der Wissenschaften zu Berlin am 24.4.1958," *Die Naturwissenschaften, 45* (1958), 221–26.

3   L. Meitner, "Max Planck als Mensch," *Die Naturwissenschaften, 45* (1958), 406–8.

4   W. Heisenberg, "Die Plancksche Entdeckung und die philosophischen Grundfragen der Atomlehre," *Die Naturwissenschaften, 45* (1958), 227–34, translated by Peter Heath in W. Heisenberg, *Across the Frontiers* (New York, 1974), pp. 8–29.

5   G. Hertz, "Die Bedeutung der Planckschen Quantentheorie für die experimentelle Physik," *Die Naturwissenschaften, 45* (1958), 401–5.

Index

Index

Index

Index

Michajłow, Włodzimierz, 36, 44
Michałowski, Kazimierz, 35
Mickiewicz, Adam, 25
Milan, 88
Milnikiel, Eugeniusz, 33, 53–54
Mises, Richard von, 117
Modzelewski, Zygmunt, 79–80
Montreal, 150
  war research in, 19, 57
Morrison, Philip, 169
Mościcki, Ignacy, 77
Moscow, 91, 107
  conference on field theory, 85–88
  Partial Test Ban Agreement, 103,
    111
Mosengeil, Kurt von, 203n
Motion and Relativity, xii, 107–8
Munich, 137

Nagasaki, 26, 179–80
Narutowicz, Gabriel, 132
Natanson, Władysław, 115–22, 130
  father of Polish theoretical physics,
    122
  impersonal manner, 120
  technically perfect lectures, 116–17
Nathan, Otto, 90, 175
Nehru, Jawaharlal, 162
Nenni, Pietro, 94–95
New Jersey, 40–41, 148
New Pathways of Science, 78
New York, 8, 25, 40, 54, 58, 145, 146
  University, 61
New Zealand, 39
Newton, Isaac, 72, 117, 155
Newtonian motion, 74, 78, 177
Nieborów, 79, 85, 108, 162

Ohrenstein, Szymon, 131
Opechowski, W., 42
Oppenheimer, Frank, 172
  in Cambridge, 164, 165
Oppenheimer, J. Robert, 161, 164–79
  and Chevalier, 170–72
  critical of Einstein, 173–75

leadership, 167
nuclear weapons, 179–80
popular lectures, 168
revered teacher, 165
trial, 168, 172–73
with generals, 167, 169
Osborne, M., 166
Ostwald, Wilhelm, 11
Ottawa, 3, 34, 47, 51, 52, 58
  National Research Council, 18–19,
    51, 58–59

Pannekoek, Anton, 9
Paris, 39, 58, 93, 105, 171, 173, 175
Pash, Boris T., 172
Pauli, Wolfgang, 44, 105, 120, 142,
    178
  on Oppenheimer, 167
  personality, 89–90
Pauling, Linus, 73, 82–83, 99
Pavlov, Ivan, 103
Peking, 93–99
Peng, H. W., 195n
Peters, Bernard, 161, 164, 172, 180
Photons, 72
Pieńkowski, Stefan, 38, 65
Pirani, Felix Arnold Edward, 187
Planck, Max, 117, 154, 181–83, 185–
    86
  Planck's constant, 181
  Planck's Law, 31
  teacher in Berlin, 182–83
Plebański, Jerzy, xii, 178
Podolsky, Boris, 177
Poincaré, Henri, 115
Poland, Academy in exile, 32–33
  Academy of Sciences, recreation
    of, 69, 78–79, 103–4, 183
  October changes in Communist
    Party, 103–5
Potkański, Polish physicist, 119
Pounder, J. R., 191n
Powell, Cecil Frank, 101–2
Poznań, 64, 120, 131
Prague, 102

Index

Princeton, 8, 40, 141, 145, 148, 154, 164, 178
  Institute for Advanced Study, 2, 4, 10, 43, 136, 137, 173
  Institute hosts Einstein-Bohr debate, 156–57
Ptolemy, 70, 74
Pugwash movement, xii, 99–103, 111

Quantum theory, 72, 141–43, 152, 155–56, 176
Quest, 6, 7, 10–12, 51

Radziwiłłs. *See* Nieborów
Rankin, John Elliott, 49
Rayski, Jerzy, 192n
Relativity, 80. *See also* Unified field theory
  general, 117, 176
  coordinate systems, 71, 74, 88, 137
  equations of motion, xi, 7, 78, 79, 82, 137, 139, 141, 143–45, 167
  field equations, xii, 5, 6, 167
  principle of, 152
  gravitational dipoles, 7, 144–45, 149
  verification of, 9
  special, 176
Riemannian matrix, 139
Roberts, R., 166
Roberts, General, 25
Robertson, Hugh Percy, 165, 166, 167
Robespierre, Maximilien, 84
Robinson, Ivor, 164
Rome, 93
Roosevelt, Franklin Delano, 21, 174, 179
Rosen, N., 177
Rosenfeld, Léon, 35
Rotblat, Joseph, 99, 102
Royal Canadian Mounted Police, 19, 26, 58
Rozental, Stefan, 126, 160–61

Rubinowicz, Wojciech, 36
Russell, Bertrand, 99
Rzewuski, Jan, 192n

Sartre, Jean-Paul, 95
Schaeffer, Clemens, 117
Schild, Alfred, ix–xii, 7, 109, 144, 160, 168, 198n
Schild, Winnie, x, xi, xii, 160
Schilpp, Paul A., 142–43, 177
Schlauch, Margaret, 193n
Schlick, Moritz, 203n
Schottky, Walter, 203n
Schrag, Lex, 57
Schroedinger, Erwin, 35
Schwarzschild, Martin, 166
Schwartz, Laurent, 43
Schwinger, Julian, 165, 166, 167
Seidenbeutlow, Efraim and Menashe, 125
Shaw, George Bernard, 35
Shugar, David, 192n
Siberia, 91
Sklodowska-Curie, Marie, 78
Slánský, Rudolf, 84
Słonimski, Antoni, 93
Smith, Sidney Earle, 47, 53
Smoluchowski, Marian, 78, 115, 116, 119
Solovine, Maurice, 10
Sommerfeld, Arnold, 73, 120, 183
Southam, Hamilton, 61
Spanish Civil War, 137, 170
Spencer, Herbert, 11
Spinoza, Baruch, 9
Stalin, Josef, 28, 86
Stalinism in Poland, 54, 75, 77, 80, 82–85, 104
Steacie, Edgar William Richard, 58–59
Stefansson, Vilhjalmur, 30
Stephenson, George, 75
Stevenson, A. F., 191n
Sun Yat-sen, 95
Sydney, Australia, 39

211